Bittker, McMahon, & Zelenak's

FEDERAL INCOME TAXATION OF INDIVIDUALS

Third Edition

Study Problems

MARTIN J. McMAHON, JR.
Clarence J. TeSelle Professor of Law,
University of Florida

LAWRENCE A. ZELENAK
Professor of Law,
Columbia University

WARREN
GORHAM
&LAMONT

A Thomson Company

Preface

THESE problem sets cover all aspects of federal income taxation that are normally the subject of an introductory course. The problems follow the sequential organization of *Federal Income Taxation of Individuals*, Third Edition, by Boris I. Bittker, Martin J. McMahon, Jr., and Lawrence A. Zelenak, and each problem set refers to the paragraphs of that text that deal with the particular facets of income tax law explored in the problem set. Chapter numbering in *Study Problems* is not consecutive, because it follows *Federal Income Taxation of Individuals* and because problems are not included for chapters that are unlikely to be used extensively in a basic tax course (i.e., Chapters 1, 2, 20, 35, 43, and 46–51). Use of these problems is not limited, however, to a course that uses *Federal Income Taxation of Individuals* as the primary text. Although the order of presentation may differ, most of the problem sets correspond to discrete sections of the leading casebooks.

The scope of *Study Problems* is comprehensive, and there are more problems than most teachers will choose to assign. Since different teachers emphasize different issues, the problems assigned may vary accordingly. Some teachers may also choose to omit repetitious problems. Such repetition arises because the same principle or rule is discussed in differing contexts in different chapters of the text, and thus there is a corresponding problem that applies that rule in the problem set for each chapter. Other teachers may assign repetitious problems for reinforcement of principles previously discussed.

To solve these problems, it is necessary to study not only the referenced paragraphs of *Federal Income Taxation of Individuals* or the assigned portions of a casebook, but also the relevant sections of the Internal Revenue Code and Treasury Regulations. Indeed, many of the problems may be solved only by referring to the Code and Regulations. Therefore, students should carefully study the sections of the Code and Regulations discussed and cited in the paragraphs of *Federal Income Taxation of Individuals* that are referred to at the beginning of the problem sets or that are assigned by the teacher in connection with each problem set.

There is a great deal of certainty in tax law. Therefore, many of these problems have correct answers, which often call for computations—sometimes complex ones. The methods of performing these computations, with examples, are found in *Federal Income Taxation of Individuals* or in the Regulations.

There is also a great deal of uncertainty in tax law. Therefore, many other problems do not have definite answers. Students may find this frustrating.

For these problems, students should try to master the arguments for and against the different possible answers and to predict which outcome—based upon an analysis of the textual discussion of cases or the reading of cases—is the one that the Internal Revenue Service would most likely reach, and which is the one the courts would most likely reach. (Their decisions are not always the same.)

Some of the questions fall into the unanswerable category because the rules of law are unclear; others fall into this category because the results in tax cases, as in all other areas of law, turn on the facts, and the facts are not fully developed. In problems of the latter type, students should apply their knowledge of the law to determine which facts must be developed to render the question answerable; they should also learn to distinguish factual issues from issues of law.

Most of these problems are realistic, although simplified in structure. Prices, property values, and interest rates, however, may deviate greatly from reality. This should be of no concern and should not affect the validity of the problems. The dollar values used in all of the problems were selected to facilitate computations and for pedagogical purposes. In one sense, however, these problems are unrealistic for students studying law. Most of them involve the tax consequences of past transactions. While lawyers frequently practice tax law when clients become embroiled in controversy with the Internal Revenue Service over the amount of tax owed, they are more frequently called upon to apply their knowledge of tax law to plan a proposed transaction. In performing this task, lawyers must analyze two or more alternative courses of conduct and advise their clients which one will produce the most advantageous tax consequences. Problems presented in such a context are, by nature, more complex than problems dealing with past transactions. In order to facilitate coverage of a greater body of substantive material in the limited time generally allotted to the introductory tax course in most law school curricula, the problems in this book focus primarily on past transactions or single proposed transactions. Many of the problems, however, contain a number of subsections in which the answers differ because one or more of the facts have been changed. Often these changes in facts would be within the control of a client acting prospectively. By carefully comparing the answers to the different variations of the facts, students should gain some appreciation of the planning function in the practice of tax law.

Finally, those students who do not want to be tax lawyers should examine the context in which the tax questions in these problems arise. Frequently—possibly more often than not—clients who go to lawyers for assistance with proposed transactions do not even know that they have tax problems. It is a lawyers' duty to recognize and solve a client's tax problems that lurk in a divorce, in a proposed settlement of an action for damages, in the purchase or sale of a business, or in the negotiation of any number of other contracts. All lawyers must—if they are to practice competently—be proficient in basic federal income tax law.

Teachers who have used the Second Edition will find that this Third Edition retains all problems from the Second Edition, except for a very few which have been rendered irrelevant by recent changes in the law. This Third Edition includes new questions relating to a number of legislative and judicial developments, including the permanent exclusion of gain on the sale of a primary residence, the higher education tax credits, the child tax credit, Roth IRAs, and the ongoing controversy concerning the proper treatment of contingent attorneys' fees. There is an old joke about the tax professor who never changes his exam questions; instead Congress just keeps changing the answers. In keeping with that joke, the Teacher's Manual has changed considerably more than the Study Problems—many familiar old questions have unfamiliar new answers.

MARTIN J. MCMAHON, JR
University of Florida

LAWRENCE ZELENAK
Columbia University

December 2002

Contents

STUDY PROBLEMS

3

The Meaning of "Income"—
Basic Definitional Concepts

PROBLEM SET 3-1

¶ 3.02 REALIZATION; ¶ 3.03 TAX-FREE IMPUTED INCOME VERSUS TAXABLE BARTER; ¶ 3.05 WINDFALL RECEIPTS–GAIN WITHOUT PAIN

(a)   Sam Scavenger spends his weekends going to flea markets, where he both buys and sells antiques and collectibles of many kinds. One day Sam purchased a picture frame from Mark Monger for $10. Almost immediately, Paula Patron offered to pay Sam $100 for the picture frame, which Paula recognized as the work of the famous woodcarver, Gepetto Pinnochio. Although Mark had overlooked this fact, Sam had been aware of it when he purchased the frame from Mark. Sam rejected Paula's offer because he planned to use the frame to hang a portrait of his family in his living room. Therefore, Sam removed the crude, and to his taste ugly, painting from the frame and planned to throw it away as worthless. However, upon removing the painting from its frame, to his surprise, he discovered that it was signed by a well-known primitive school artist. Sam kept the painting, which shortly thereafter was appraised at a value of $10,000. Has Sam realized any taxable income as a result of these events?

(b)   Suppose a taxpayer owns property that increases in value by $5,000 during a particular year. Because of the rule that unrealized appreciation is not taxed, the taxpayer pays no tax on the $5,000. However, if the taxpayer later sells the property, she will then realize and pay tax on the $5,000 appreciation that occurred in the earlier year (assuming the $5,000 increase in value was not offset by a decrease in value in a later year). Suppose, in this case, the taxpayer realizes the gain and pays tax on it ten years after the year in which the appreciation occurred. Assuming the tax rate is 20 percent in both years, what is the advantage (if any) to the taxpayer of deferring the tax until the recognition of the gain?

1

PROBLEM SET 3-2

¶ 3.03 TAX-FREE IMPUTED INCOME VERSUS TAXABLE BARTER

(a)   Would the income tax system be fairer if homeowners were taxed on the imputed rental value of their homes? Can the argument that exclusion of imputed rental income is unfair to those who rent rather than own homes be satisfactorily dismissed by responding that everyone is free to rent or own, and must accept the tax consequences attendant on that choice?

(b)   (1)   Many automobile dealers offer new automobiles for lease as well as for sale. If it is proper to tax homeowners on the imputed rental value of their homes, should automobile owners be taxed on the imputed rental value of their automobiles?

        (2)   Furniture, televisions, and other major appliances may also be rented rather than purchased. Where should the inclusion of the imputed rental value of owner-used property stop? Is the difficulty in setting limits a valid reason to continue to exclude all imputed rental income?

(c)   Would the fairness and efficiency of the income tax system be improved if the system taxed the imputed income of full-time homemakers? Is there any administratively feasible way of imposing such a tax?

PROBLEM SET 3-3

¶ 3.03 TAX-FREE IMPUTED INCOME VERSUS TAXABLE BARTER

(a)   Betty Barrister was engaged by Carl Condo to defend Carl on a criminal charge of driving under the influence of alcohol. Normally, Betty would charge $600 to represent a client in such a case. Through Betty's efforts, Carl was acquitted. A grateful Carl offered Betty two weeks' use of his condominium at Hilton Head Island, South Carolina, which normally rents for $300 per week, in lieu of a cash payment of the fee. Betty accepted this offer and enjoyed her two-week vacation in June. Have Betty and Carl realized gross income as a result of this transaction?

(b)   When Betty returned from her vacation (in part (a)), she discovered her law partner, Sam Solicitor, also required her services for a defense against a drunk driving charge. Betty successfully defended Sam, but kept no time records, and the partners made no attempt to account for this work in the division of the partnership's profits. At another time, Sam prepared new wills for both Betty and her husband. Again, no records were kept of the work in the partnership books. Sam's services, however, like Betty's, would have cost a client $600. Have Sam and Betty realized gross income as a result of these events?

(c)   While Betty was on vacation at Hilton Head Island, her neighbor Hank Handy cut Betty's lawn twice, as a favor to Betty. After Betty returned from vacation, Hank went on vacation, and Betty promised to return the favor. Betty cut Hank's lawn the first week. Betty decided that she would rather play tennis the second week, so she paid a teenage boy who lived next door $10 to cut Hank's lawn. Have Betty and Hank realized gross income as a result of these events?

(d)   If you did not reach the same conclusion in each of the above cases, how do you justify your different decisions?

(e)   The Friendly National Bank normally charges various service fees to its checking account customers—a basic monthly fee of $5, plus twenty-five cents for every check written on an account, and $1 for every use of an automated teller machine. All these service charges are waived, however, for a customer who maintains a minimum balance of $1,000 in a non-interest bearing checking account. Beth gets free banking services under this arrangement. Does Beth have income under IRC § 61 as a result?

PROBLEM SET 3-4

¶ 3.04 "GAIN"—TAX-FREE RECOVERY OF CAPITAL

(a)   Last year, Cindy Creditor lent Danny Debtor $1,000. This year, Danny repaid $1,200 to Cindy, as had been agreed. How much gross income has Cindy realized?

(b)   Sam Suburbia purchased a tree-filled house lot for $50,000, on which he planned to construct his dream home. Before construction work on the lot began, Paul Bunyan, who owned the lot next door, built a home there. To provide more sun for his greenhouse, Paul cut down a large number of trees on Sam's lot and used them for firewood. An outraged Sam sued Paul and collected $10,000 for combined damages representing a decrease in value of his lot and conversion of the cut timber. How much gross income must Sam recognize?

(c)   Candy Consumer purchased a new microwave oven at the local Q-Mart store for $400. Conglomerate Corp., the manufacturer of the oven, was offering a $50 rebate to the purchaser, paid directly from Conglomerate Corp. upon the purchaser's request accompanied by proof of purchase. Candy mailed a request for a rebate that was promptly honored. Must Candy include the $50 received from Conglomerate Corp. in her gross income?

(d)   Danny Dealer is a self-employed importer of Colombian marijuana. During the last taxable year, Danny paid $500,000 for purchases of marijuana in Colombia, incurred $200,000 of expenses in transporting the marijuana to Miami, and sold the marijuana on a tarmac in Miami for $2 million. Being an honest and respectable citizen in all other ways, Danny has consulted you with respect to his federal income tax liability. How much gross income did Danny realize from his business last year? (See IRC §§ 263A(a)(2), 280E; Treas. Reg. § 1.61-3(a).)

PROBLEM SET 3-5

¶ 3.05 WINDFALL RECEIPTS—GAIN WITHOUT PAIN

(a)   Sam Scavenger recently purchased an old vase stuffed with artificial flowers at a flea market for $10. While cleaning the vase, Sam discovered an antique ruby brooch at the bottom, beneath some old newspaper that had been wedged in to hold the flowers in place. Shortly thereafter, Sam had both the brooch and the vase appraised; each was worth $500. How much gross income has Sam realized as a result of these events?

(b)   Rhonda Revue is the book editor for the Possum Trot Sunday Times newspaper. In that capacity, she frequently receives complimentary copies of recently published books from publishers. Last year, she received 100 books with an aggregate fair market value of $2,500. All books but one remain in her office. Without ever reading or reviewing it, Rhonda gave a new copy of The Encyclopedia of Incorrect Trivia, which had a retail price of $50, to her son-in-law for Christmas. Must Rhonda include as income the value of any of the books?

PROBLEM SET 3-6

¶ 3.06 REIMBURSEMENT FOR WRONGFUL DEATH OR PERSONAL INJURY

(a)   Andy Accountant attended a party given by one of his clients, Suzie Superstar. Soon thereafter, The National Trash, a scandal sheet, published an article about the wild activities of the guests at the party, naming all of the guests, including Andy. Although the facts of the article were entirely true, Andy prevailed in a suit against The National Trash and collected $200,000 of compensatory damages for invasion of privacy and $100,000 of punitive damages. To what extent must Andy include the $300,000 damages in his gross income?

PROBLEM SET 3-7

¶ 3.07 THE RECOVERY OF DEDUCTED ITEMS—TAX BENEFIT PRINCIPLES

(a)   Last year, Henry Homeowner had $20,000 of gross income and paid $2,000 in local real estate taxes, which were deductible under IRC § 164. However, Henry claimed no itemized deductions when computing his income taxes, because his total itemized deductions did not exceed the standard deduction. This year, pursuant to a state court decision ruling the prior year's real estate tax assessments invalid, Henry received a tax rebate of $200 from the city.

　　　　(1)   How much of the $200 must Henry include in his gross income this year?

       (2)   How would your answer be different if Henry were married, with no dependents, filed a joint return, and had itemized deductions for $2,000 of real estate taxes and $3,150 of home mortgage interest (under IRC § 163)? (Assume the standard deduction would have been $5,000.)

       (3)   How would your answer be different in part (a)(2) above if Henry had also deducted $500 for state income taxes?

(b)   Last Fast Food, Inc., which owned the Local Quickie-Burger franchise, hired Izzy Itinerant to paint the exterior of the restaurant building. When Izzy was done, Last Fast Food, Inc., issued him a check for $1,000 dated November 30, which bore the legend "void if not cashed within 90 days." In computing last year's income taxes, Last Fast Food, Inc., properly deducted the $1,000 as a business expense under IRC § 162. Izzy has never cashed the check despite the lapse of over a year, and the bank will no longer honor the check. Last Fast Food, Inc., has no knowledge of Izzy's whereabouts, his telephone has been disconnected, and he is no longer listed with the city directory or with the Chamber of Commerce. Must Last Fast Food, Inc., include the previously deducted $1,000 in income this year?

PROBLEM SET 3-8

¶ 3.08 INDIRECT RECEIPTS: PAYMENT OF TAXPAYER'S EXPENSES AND BARGAIN PURCHASES

(a)   Toxic Chemical Corp. failed to treat its waste before discharging it into the Ohio River because the board of directors had decided it would be cost-efficient not to do so, as long as the company's actions went undetected. Unfortunately, Toxic was caught in the act, and, pursuant to federal pollution control statutes, the government commenced criminal action against Toxic and its individual directors. Toxic and each member of the board of directors pleaded guilty, and each was fined $10,000. Toxic promptly paid the federal government $100,000, which represented the fines assessed against it and each of its nine directors. Must the directors of Toxic recognize any gross income?

(b)   The Los Francisco Faultlines of the recently formed World Indoor Football League have agreed to pay Jack Sweatshirt, the winner of last year's Heisman Trophy, $2 million (after taxes) to sign a contract to play football for the Faultlines next year. Assuming that Jack has no other income and is entitled to no deductions, and that the income tax rate is a flat 20 percent, what will be his salary next year (for purposes of computing his gross income)?

(c)   (1)   Lynn Lawyer recently joined the law firm of Helvering & Guy as an associate. When Lynn purchased a home, she obtained a mortgage from the Last National Bank of Metropolis, which is a client of Helvering & Guy. As a courtesy, because of the relationship between the bank and the law firm, the bank waived its normal $500 loan application fee when Lynn's application was processed. Must Lynn recognize any gross income as a result of the waiver by the bank of the loan application fee?

     (2)   Lynn's loan application was approved, and the bank also waived the loan origination fee of $1,000 that it usually charges customers whose loan applications are approved. If Lynn had paid the loan origination fee, it would have been currently deductible under IRC §§ 163(h)(3) and 461(g)(2). Must Lynn recognize any gross income as a result of the waiver by the bank of the loan origination fee?

(d)   Jane sued her former employer for employment discrimination under Title VII of the Civil Rights Act, and was awarded damages of $600,000. The employer paid the $600,000 to Jane's attorney, who transferred $400,000 to Jane and kept the other $200,000 as his one-third contingent fee (pursuant to his fee arrangement with Jane). How much ($600,000 or $400,000) must Jane include in her gross income? Is there any practical difference between (1) including only $400,000 in gross income and (2) including $600,000 in gross income and claiming a $200,000 deduction for the attorney's fee?

4

Income—The Effect of
Offsetting Liabilities

PROBLEM SET 4-1

¶ 4.02 NOMINAL VERSUS BENEFICIAL OWNERSHIP—AMOUNTS RECEIVED BY TRUSTEES, NOMINEES, AGENTS, AND OTHER CONDUITS

(a)   Mike Moonshine operates an illegal distillery in Dry County. The Dry County local government, pursuant to state statute, submitted a referendum to the voters of Dry County on whether packaged liquor sales should be legalized in Dry County. Mike, who was vigorously opposed to legal liquor sales, collected $10,000, mostly in contributions of $5 to $10, from local citizens opposed to legalized liquor sales. Mike promised all of the contributors that he would spend the funds to oppose the referendum in the name of the Dry County Temperance Society, an organization that, in fact, apart from Mike, did not exist. All of the money was deposited in a bank account in the name of the Dry County Temperance Society. Mike had sole signatory authority on the bank account. Of this money, $9,000 was spent for advertising in opposition to the referendum. The remaining $1,000 was used by Mike to purchase new distilling equipment after the voters rejected the referendum to legalize the sale of liquor. How much gross income has Mike realized as a result of these events?

PROBLEM SET 4-2

¶ 4.03 AMOUNTS RECEIVED UNDER "CLAIM OF RIGHT"

(a)   Last year Paul Prez, who owns 90 percent of the stock of Prez Corp., received $50,000 in salary and a $100,000 bonus from Prez Corp. These amounts were paid pursuant to a written employment contract that obligated Paul to repay any portion of the bonus that the IRS, in an audit, determined was a dividend rather than a bonus. When it audited

9

Prez Corp. this year, the IRS determined that $50,000 of the purported $100,000 bonus was really a dividend. Accordingly, Paul promptly repaid $50,000 to Prez Corp. May Paul compute his tax liability for this year using IRC § 1341?

(b)   Assume that Paul is single, has no children, and had no itemized deductions last year or this year. Consider these two situations:

    (1)   Last year Paul had no income other than what he received from Prez Corp., and this year he has taxable income of $300,000 (without the $50,000 deduction).

    (2)   Last year Paul had no income other than what he received from Prez Corp., and this year he has taxable income of $75,000 (without the $50,000 deduction).

For each situation, if he can, should Paul take advantage of IRC § 1341(a)(5)? Why or why not?

PROBLEM SET 4-3

¶ 4.04 SECURITY DEPOSITS

(a)   (1)   Donna Disc, the proprietor of the Saturday Night Disco, recently relocated to the Galleria Mall, a new enclosed shopping center. The owner of the mall, Shelter Associates, required a $10,000 security deposit from Donna. Shelter Associates may retain the deposit for the entire original ten-year lease term (and any extensions), but must return it within sixty days of termination of the lease, after deducting any amounts necessary to repair any damages to the premises caused by Donna's occupancy. While it holds the security deposit, Shelter Associates may commingle the deposit with its own funds and need not pay Donna any interest. Must Shelter Associates include the $10,000 security deposit as gross income when it is received? What will be the tax consequences of repayment of the security deposit upon termination of the lease?

    (2)   Would your answer to part (a)(1) differ if Shelter Associates were required to segregate the $10,000 in a separate account in the name of Shelter Associates as trustee for Donna Disc, and

any interest earned on the account were added to the security deposit and repaid to Donna upon termination of the lease? Who should include the interest as income as it is earned?

(3)   Would your answer to part (a)(1) be different if Shelter Associates were required to segregate the $10,000 in a separate bank account in the name of "Shelter Associates as trustee for Donna Disc" and Shelter Associates were entitled to withdraw any interest earned on the deposit?

(4)   Would your answer to part (a)(1) be different if the purpose of the deposit were to secure the payment of rent under the lease?

PROBLEM SET 4-4

¶ 4.05 DISCHARGE OF DEBT FOR LESS THAN FACE AMOUNT

(a)   Donald Debtor borrowed $10,000 from Claire Creditor a few years ago. The loan was unsecured, bore adequate interest that has been paid by Donald, and was used by Donald to purchase a variety of consumer goods for personal use. However, Donald has now fallen on hard times. He owes his creditors, including Claire, $100,000, but he has only $95,000 of assets, consisting of the following: $7,500 in cash; 100 shares of stock of Specific Motors Corp., with a basis of $5,000 and a fair market value of $7,500; and a condominium in which he lives that has a fair market value of $80,000 and a basis of $50,000. Donald has asked Claire if he can make some arrangement to reduce the amount of the debt. How much gross income must Donald report under the following alternative arrangements with Claire?

(1)   Donald pays Claire $7,500, and Claire cancels the promissory note.   61 (a) C(2)

(2)   Donald transfers 100 shares of stock of Specific Motors Corp. (which has an aggregate fair market value of $7,500 and a basis of $5,000) to Claire, and Claire cancels the promissory note. What will be Donald's basis in his condominium after this transaction?   Sec C108 (e) (8)

(3)   Donald, who is a carpenter, performs renovation work on Claire's house. Normally, Donald would charge $7,500 for these services, but instead Claire cancels the promissory note.

(b)   Several years ago, Tommy Trucker borrowed $50,000 from the Last National Bank, with which he purchased a used tractor-trailer rig and went into business as an independent trucker. Tommy has not yet made any principal payments on the loan, but has paid all the interest due. Tommy's business has not been doing well, and his only assets are $30,000 in cash and the tractor-trailer, which is now worth $25,000. The loan is his only debt. If the Last National Bank accepts $30,000 in cash from Tommy in full discharge of his debt, how much must Tommy include in his gross income?

(c)   Several years ago, Tammy Tenement borrowed $50,000 from the Penultimate National Bank, with which she purchased a duplex apartment building that she held for rental purposes and that was mortgaged to the bank to secure the loan. Tammy has not made any principal payments on the loan, but has paid all of the interest due. Tammy's duplex has been vacant for some time, and her only assets are $30,000 in cash and the duplex, which is now worth $25,000 and which has an adjusted basis of $48,000. The loan is her only debt. If the Penultimate Bank accepts $30,000 in cash from Tammy in full discharge of her debt, how much must Tammy include in income?

(d)   Jim and Bob Double are twin brothers who work in identical jobs that pay $40,000 a year. Last year, they each borrowed $1,500 from the Last National Bank for a vacation in Las Vegas, where they both spent their entire loan proceeds. This year, Jim dutifully used $1,500 of his wages to repay the Last National Bank. However, Bob not only failed to repay the bank, but he also spent all of his wages and filed for bankruptcy. Bob's debt to the bank was discharged. Jim, whose total assets were the same as Bob's—none—wants to know why he is required to pay taxes on the wages he used to repay the loan that paid for his vacation, while his no-good brother, who will never repay the loan, also will never have to pay taxes on the $1,500 that paid for his vacation. Explain to Jim why this rule is fair.

(e)   Gary Grad borrowed $10,000 from Alma Mater University over the course of several years while pursuing his college degree in civil engineering. Following graduation, Gary began working for Grad Construction Co., which was owned by Gary's father. His father was so happy that Gary had rejected more lucrative offers of employment

12

from larger firms to join his small company that he paid off Gary's educational loans. Must Gary recognize any gross income?

(f)   Last June, Andy Auto took his car to Frank Fixit for some repairs. When the work was done, Andy paid the bill with a $500 check. How much gross income has Andy realized if the check is not cashed in the following situations?

    (1)   The check was returned for insufficient funds because Andy had made an arithmetic error in his checkbook. Frank subsequently lost the check, and it was never deposited. Although Andy wondered why the check never cleared, he never called Frank. The statute of limitations on Frank's claim expired last April.

    (2)   The next day, Andy discovered that the repairs were poorly performed. Andy immediately ordered his bank to stop payment on the check, which it did, and Andy sent Frank a check for $250, with a note saying that was all he thought the repairs were worth. Frank cashed the check, and, although he sent several letters demanding payment of the additional $250, he never filed suit, and the statute of limitations expired last April.

(g)   Paula Ped sued Bo Biker for injuries Paula suffered when Bo negligently ran over Paula as she was crossing the street. The court entered a judgment of $50,000 in Paula's favor in 2002. Although Bo was solvent, Bo did everything he could to hinder Paula from collecting on the judgment. Finally, in 2003, Paula agreed to accept $40,000 cash from Bo and to cancel the other $10,000 of the judgment. Does Bo have cancellation of indebtedness income in the following situations?

    (1)   The accident occurred while Bo was driving for personal purposes, so Bo never claimed a deduction for the $50,000 judgment.

    (2)   The accident occurred as Bo was driving in connection with his business. As an accrual basis taxpayer, Bo properly deducted the $50,000 judgment as a business expense in 2002.

PROBLEM SET 4-5

¶ 4.06 UNLAWFUL ACTIVITIES

(a)   Paul Pyramid, a former stockbroker, devised a new investment program that he dubbed the "Fool and His Money Share Account Investment Program." Paul's plan involved investors entrusting him with their funds, which he promised would be invested on their behalf. Paul told the investors that they would earn a guaranteed yield of 5 percent above the yield of U.S. Treasury bills and that they could withdraw their investment any time they wished. Paul also told them that the portfolio was so complex that he could not provide them with detailed information on how he invested the funds. Last year, Paul received $1 million from the investors. Paul never maintained any structured investment program, although he did purchase Treasury bills in his own name with $500,000 of the funds. He used $150,000 of the funds to pay the "yield" to the investors and returned another $50,000 to those investors who withdrew from the program. The remaining $300,000 was spent by Paul to maintain the lifestyle he believed appropriate for a financial expert of his ability. How much of the $1 million collected by Paul last year must be included in his gross income?

5

Gifts, Bequests, Prizes, and Scholarships

PROBLEM SET 5-1

¶ 5.01 GIFTS AND BEQUESTS GENERALLY; ¶ 5.02 EXCLUSION OF GIFTS FROM GROSS INCOME

(a)   The law firm of Barrister & Solicitor employs five secretaries and two paralegals. Two years ago, each employee received a $15 turkey as a Christmas present from the partners. Last year, the partners gave each employee a $15 gift certificate from Tears Sawbuck Department Store. This year, the partners gave each employee an additional $15 in his or her paycheck for Christmas. For the purpose of filing informational tax forms with the IRS that report the total compensation paid to each employee in each year, how should the law firm treat the Christmas presents in each year?

(b)   Every Christmas, Larry Lawyer receives a variety of bottles of liquor and foodstuffs, such as hams, turkeys, and cheese baskets, from a number of his clients. Although a single client rarely gives Larry anything that costs more than $15, the total value of all these Christmas presents is probably $500 to $600. Should Larry report the value of these gifts as gross income?

(c)   Peter Professor adopted the abridged student edition of *Federal Income Taxation of Partnerships and Corporations* for use in his tax course at Ivy University Law School. Following the adoption of the text, Wriggley Publishers provided Peter with a complimentary copy of the unabridged professional edition of the book, which it normally sells for $125. Wriggley Publishers' policy is to provide a complimentary copy of the abridged student edition to any tax professor who teaches a course in which the book might be used, but it provides complimentary copies of the professional edition only to professors who have adopted the abridged student edition for use in their classes. Must Peter

15

recognize any gross income as a result of receiving the professional edition from Wriggley Publishers?

(d)   (1)   Ronnie Retiree had worked as a prop man at Tiger Movie Studios for fifty years. Upon Ronnie's retirement, his co-workers decided to collect enough money to buy Ronnie a new aluminum fishing boat and a twenty-horsepower outboard motor, which together cost $2,000: The forty workers in Ronnie's department contributed a total of $1,600. When the department manager learned that they were $400 short of their goal, he arranged for Tiger Movie Studios to contribute the remaining $400. Did Ronnie realize any gross income when he received the boat and motor?

         (2)   Would your answer be different if Ronnie were given the $2,000 in cash instead of the boat and motor?

(e)   Bertha Blueblood was quite displeased when her son Biffy announced his engagement to Roxie Punker, who was, according to Bertha, from the "wrong side of the tracks." To forestall the impending marriage, Bertha promised Biffy that she would give him $2 million to break his engagement to Roxie and marry Muffy Straitlace. Having inherited his sense of priorities, Biffy accepted the offer. Must Biffy include the $2 million in his gross income?

(f)   (1)   Is it clear that restaurant tips are not gifts under the *Duberstein* criteria? What if a generous customer, impressed with the service, leaves a 25 percent tip instead of the customary 15 percent?

         (2)   Ricardo's is a rather elegant restaurant, which has twenty employees on a normal business day. Last year Ricardo's had gross receipts from food and beverage sales of $1 million. Ricardo's employees reported to Ricardo's (pursuant to IRC § 6053(a)) receiving only $50,000 (5 percent of gross receipts) in tips. In reality, the average tip at Ricardo's is almost 15 percent. Will the employees succeed in avoiding tax on any unreported tips?

         (3)   Would it be better for Congress and the IRS to wink at the underreporting of tip income, because most tip recipients are struggling just to get by?

(g)   Mike Manager was employed by Greater Gadget Corp. for many years before his death. At the time of his death last November, Greater Gadget owed Mike $1,000 of accrued but unpaid salary, which was then paid to Mary, Mike's widow. In December, the board of directors, in recognition of Mike's contribution to the success of the business, voted to pay Mary an additional $15,000. To what extent (if at all) may each of the two payments to Mary be excluded from her gross income?

PROBLEM SET 5-2

¶ 5.03 EXCLUSION OF INHERITED PROPERTY FROM GROSS INCOME

(a)   Millie Med was a physician specializing in family practice in a rural town. Her patient load was increasing quite rapidly, and her health was failing just as rapidly. Anticipating the future, Millie made a promise to her niece, Denise Doc (who had just graduated from State University Medical School), to pay off Denise's medical school loans and also to include a provision in her will directing her executor to pay off the loans if she died before they had been paid in full, if Denise would join her medical practice. Denise accepted. Millie changed her will as promised and, as it happened, died shortly thereafter. When Millie's executor pays Denise's outstanding educational loans, must Denise recognize those payments as gross income?

PROBLEM SET 5-3

¶ 5.05 PRIZES AND AWARDS

(a)   While on an errand to buy some disposable diapers, Sam Shopper was the one millionth customer to walk through the doors of the Gotham City G-Mart Discount Department Store. In recognition of this achievement, G-Mart gave Sam his choice of $100 in cash or a new Omicrona watch. G-Mart had paid $100 for the watch and normally sells it for $175, but that day G-Mart was advertising that particular model as a sale item for $150. The same watch retailed for $200 in Eddie's Exclusive Jewelers across the street from G-Mart. If Sam wanted to sell the watch, he could get $125 at Paul's Pawn Shop. Sam chose the watch and kept it. How much gross income must he recognize?

(b)   Willy Winner appeared as a contestant on a television game show and won an all expenses-paid, two-week vacation in Hawaii for four people. The trip included airfare, lodging, and meals. The fair market value of the trip was usually $8,000 ($2,000 per person). The only conditions to the prize were that Willy use it personally and take the vacation within six months of the date on which he won it. Willy took his wife and two children on vacation with him. If Willy had purchased the vacation himself, the hotel would have provided a "family discount" of $500, and the airline would have provided a "family fare discount" of another $500. How much gross income must Willy recognize? What if Willy is in the 40 percent tax bracket, and the subjective value of the prize to him is only $2,000?

(c)   Linda Lawstudent was a third-year student at Ivory Tower University Law School. Linda wrote a paper for a seminar on "The International Law Aspects of Killer-Spy Satellites." Her professor recommended that Linda submit the paper to a writing competition sponsored by the American Bar Association Section on Law and Counterintelligence Activities. Linda did so and won second prize—a handsome certificate and $250 in cash. How much must Linda include in her gross income? Would your answer be different if the professor had submitted the paper in Linda's name?

PROBLEM SET 5-4

¶ 5.06 SCHOLARSHIPS

(a)   Lucy entered and won the Miss Oregon Beauty, Talent, and Personality Pageant, sponsored by the Oregon Tourist Board. As Miss Oregon, Lucy received a $10,000 scholarship from the Tourist Board, to be paid directly to the college she attended. This scholarship would pay for her tuition, room, board, fees, and books. The scholarship is increased to $20,000 if the winner takes a year off from school to tour North America promoting Oregon tourism, making publicity appearances, attending supermarket openings, county fairs, and so forth. The winner has no obligation to do so, however, and can choose to take only the $10,000 scholarship. Lucy chose to spend a year touring as Miss Oregon and received the $20,000 scholarship, which she used to attend the college of her choice. How much income must Lucy recognize upon receipt of the scholarship?

(b)   Harry Halfback was the star player on his high school football team and was the most recruited high school football player in the country last year. Harry chose to attend Pigskin University, which offered Harry a full tuition scholarship. The only condition of the scholarship was that Harry maintain a sufficient grade point average to stay in school. However, the scholarship was awarded for only one year at a time, and there was no guarantee that it would be renewed for the next year if Harry did not play on the Pigskin football team the prior year. Is Harry's scholarship tax-exempt?

(c)   Gertrude Grad is studying for her Ph.D. in English at Ivy University. Her tuition is $25,000 per year. This year, she received a $15,000 scholarship from the university. She was required to teach a section of freshman English composition as a condition of the scholarship. Other teaching assistants, who are not students at the university, are paid $5,000 by the university for teaching a section of composition. She received no other financial assistance of any kind. How much, if any, of her scholarship is taxable?

(d)   Specific Electric Corp. has a formal program under which it awards three scholarships to employees in the engineering department. To be eligible, an employee must have been employed by the company for five years and want to pursue a Ph.D. in electrical engineering. The only other condition of the scholarship award is that the employee not accept a job with a different employer after completing the degree requirements, without first giving Specific Electric an opportunity to match the competitor's offer. However, the promotional literature providing information about the scholarship that is distributed to the employees states that they are "expected" to return to their employment at Specific Electric following the earning of their degrees. This year Eddie Engineer applied for and received a $40,000 scholarship to pay for tuition, books, and living expenses for himself and his family while pursuing a Ph.D. at Daytona Beach Tech. Is Eddie's scholarship tax-exempt under IRC § 117?

6

Life Insurance, Annuities, and Employee Death Benefits

PROBLEM SET 6-1

¶ 6.01 INSURANCE, ANNUITY AND ENDOWMENT CONTRACTS: IN GENERAL; ¶ 6.02 LIFE INSURANCE PROCEEDS PAID AT DEATH; ¶ 6.04 OTHER RECEIPTS UNDER LIFE INSURANCE, ANNUITY, AND ENDOWMENT CONTRACTS

(a)   (1)   Irene Insured, who owned a $50,000 whole life insurance policy, died last year. The insurance company paid her husband Ivan the $50,000 face value of the policy. Must Ivan include the proceeds in his gross income?

        (2)   What would be your answer if Ivan elected a settlement option under which the insurance company would pay him annually the interest earned on the $50,000 (which is expected to be $4,000), with the $50,000 payable upon his death to his daughter Inez? Will Inez realize gross income when she receives the $50,000 upon Ivan's death?

        (3)   What would be your answer if Ivan elected to receive an annuity of $4,700 annually for the remainder of his life (Ivan's life expectancy is twenty-five years), and there is no refund feature if Ivan were to die before receiving payments for twenty-five years?

        (4)   What would have been the tax consequences if Irene, after having paid aggregate premiums of $30,000 on the insurance policy, had surrendered it for its cash surrender value of $40,000 the day before she died unexpectedly?

PROBLEM SET 6-2

¶ 6.02 LIFE INSURANCE PROCEEDS PAID AT DEATH; ¶ 6.04 OTHER RECEIPTS UNDER LIFE INSURANCE, ANNUITY, AND ENDOWMENT CONTRACTS; ¶ 6.05 DEDUCTIBILITY OF PREMIUMS AND LOSSES

(a)   Benny Businessman and Eddie Entrepreneur were partners in a real estate development business. Benny and Eddie purchased life insurance policies on each other's lives, naming the insured partner's wife as beneficiary. They agreed that upon one or the other's death, the entire business would belong to the surviving partner, in exchange for the payment of the insurance proceeds. In the year the insurance was purchased, Benny and Eddie each paid a premium of $600. Later that year Eddie died, $100,000 was paid by the insurance company to Eddie's widow, and Benny became sole owner of the business. What are the tax consequences of these events for Benny and Eddie's widow?

(b)   Shortly after Eddie's death, Benny formed a new partnership with Danny Developer. Benny entered into a reciprocal insurance arrangement with Danny similar to the one he had with Eddie. Rather than taking out additional insurance, Danny purchased from Eddie's widow for $800 the existing insurance policy on Benny's life. Danny paid an additional premium of $500. When Benny died, the insurance company paid Benny's widow $100,000, and Danny became sole owner of the business. What are the tax consequences to Danny and to Benny's widow?

(c)   John is in the later stages of AIDS. His doctor has told him he has, at most, twenty-four months to live. John owns a life insurance policy with a death benefit of $200,000. The policy provides that John may elect, in lieu of the death benefit, an "accelerated death benefit" (ADB), upon being diagnosed as reasonably expected to die in the next twenty-four months. John so elects. The amount of the ADB is $181,400, which is the present value of $200,000 payable in two years, using a 5 percent discount rate (which is the interest rate applicable to policy loans under the insurance contract). John intends to use the money to pay for medical expenses not covered by his insurance. Is the ADB excludable from John's income under IRC § 101?

PROBLEM SET 6-3

¶ 6.03 ANNUITY PAYMENTS

(a)   (1)   Phil Pensioner purchased an annuity from Insurance Co. for a lump-sum premium of $10,000. The annuity will pay Phil $1,490 a year for the remainder of his life. Phil's life expectancy is ten years. When Phil receives his first annual payment of $1,490, what are the tax consequences?

        (2)   As it turns out, Phil survives beyond his ten-year life expectancy. When he receives his eleventh annual payment of $1,490, what are the tax consequences?

        (3)   Suppose, instead, that Phil dies after having received only six payments, and that the annuity provides for no payments of any kind after his death. Are there any income tax consequences of his death?

(b)   (1)   Nick and Nora Newlywed purchased a College Endowment Policy from Insurance Co. after the birth of their first child. Under the policy, Nick and Nora paid $1,000 per year for eighteen years to Insurance Co. The policy provided that at the end of eighteen years Insurance Co. would pay Nick and Nora $37,500 in cash or a larger amount over several years. After paying premiums for eighteen years, they elected, pursuant to the terms of the policy, to receive $11,850 a year for four years. How much of each payment must they include in their gross income? (Assume neither IRC § 529 nor IRC § 530 applies.)

        (2)   The policy provides that, at any time before the child reaches the age of 18, Nick and Nora may borrow against the cash value of the policy. When the child is 15, and they have paid $15,000 in premiums, they borrow $25,000 against the policy (the loan is nonrecourse and secured by the policy). Do they have income as a result of this loan?

7

Compensation for Personal Injuries and Sickness

PROBLEM SET 7-1

¶ 7.01 COMPENSATION FOR PERSONAL INJURIES AND SICKNESS; ¶ 7.02 WORKERS' COMPENSATION, DISABILITY BENEFITS, AND ACCIDENT AND HEALTH INSURANCE PROCEEDS; ¶ 7.03 DAMAGES RECEIVED ON ACCOUNT OF PERSONAL PHYSICAL INJURIES OR SICKNESS

(a)   Pam Pedestrian was seriously injured when Andy Auto ran a red light and struck Pam with his automobile. Pam sued Andy for $100,000, alleging damages of $20,000 for past medical expenses, $10,000 for future medical expenses, $30,000 for lost wages, and $40,000 for pain and suffering.

    (1)   After the trial, the jury awarded $100,000 to Pam, which was paid by Andy's insurance company. How much gross income must Pam recognize?

    (2)   How would your answer be different if the case were settled out of court, with Andy's insurance company paying Pam $60,000?

    (3)   How would your answer be different if the jury awarded Pam only $70,000, because Pam's employer continued to pay her despite her injury?

(b)   Wally Worker was injured when Charley Coworker dropped a wrench on Wally's head. Wally missed six months of work and received $100 per week pursuant to the state workers' compensation law. Wally's employer voluntarily paid Wally another $25 per week. How much gross income must Wally recognize?

(c)   (1)   Paula Policewoman was permanently disabled in the line of duty at age 40 and was no longer able to work as a police officer. Paula received a disability retirement pension of $200 per week, which will continue as a retirement pension after she reaches age 55. Paula is single and has no other source of income. To what extent will Paula's pension be excluded from gross income under IRC § 104 or IRC § 105? May she claim a credit under IRC § 22?

        (2)   How would your answer be different if Paula's injury had not occurred in the line of duty, but she received the same benefits?

(d)   Payne N. Suffering was injured through the negligence of an employee of Saints Preserve and Protectus Hospital. In the course of settlement negotiations, the hospital's insurance company has given Payne the choice of two alternatives: a lump-sum settlement of $100,000, payable immediately, or a "structured settlement," under which Payne would receive $10,000 a year for twenty years and $100,000 at the end of the twenty years. If Payne takes the $100,000 lump sum, he will invest it in a taxable twenty-year bond paying $10,000 interest annually. Which offer should Payne prefer?

(e)   Should the jury in a personal injury case be informed that any amount it may award for lost wages will be nontaxable? Why or why not?

(f)   Bob sued Carl for intentional infliction of emotional distress, in a jurisdiction in which physical manifestation of the distress is an element of the prima facie case. The jury awarded Bob damages of $100,000, of which $90,000 was for pain and suffering and $10,000 was for medical expenses. How much of the award (if any) must Bob include in his gross income?

8

Employee Fringe Benefits

PROBLEM SET 8-1

¶ 8.02 EMPLOYER-FINANCED ACCIDENT AND HEALTH INSURANCE

(a)   (1)   Fred Foreman's employer paid $3,000 of medical insurance premiums last year for a family medical insurance policy for Fred. The employer provided the same benefits for all of its employees. Fred's wife was hospitalized, and the insurance company paid $10,000 directly to the medical provider. This covered 100 percent of her medical expenses. Must Fred include either or both the medical insurance premiums and proceeds in his gross income?

       (2)   How would your answer be different if, in addition to the $10,000 insurance payment attributable to the employer-provided insurance, Fred received $2,000 from an individual hospitalization policy that he purchased after reading an advertisement in the Sunday newspaper? (In other words, the two policies together paid $12,000 on account of only $10,000 of medical expenses.)

(b)   (1)   The medical professional corporation of Harte, Kidnee & Braine maintains medical insurance policies only for its employees who are licensed physicians. The corporation employs four physicians: Doctors Harte, Kidnee, and Braine (all shareholders), and Dr. Livers (not a shareholder). It also employs twelve nurses. Last year, the corporation paid $2,000 of medical insurance premiums for each physician. How much gross income, if any, have the doctors realized as a result of their insurance coverage?

       (2)   The corporation also provides for uninsured reimbursement of dental expenses for all employees who are licensed physicians. Dr. Harte was reimbursed for $2,000 of dental expenses, and Dr. Livers was reimbursed for $1,000 of dental expenses. Must either of them recognize any gross income?

PROBLEM SET 8-2

¶ 8.01 INTRODUCTION; ¶ 8.10 MISCELLANEOUS FRINGE BENEFITS; SEE ALSO ¶ 8.11 EMPLOYEE-CHOSEN BENEFITS ("CAFETERIA PLANS")

(a)   (1)   Employees of Agony Airlines are allowed to fly free on any scheduled flight, but only on a standby basis. Francis Flight flew free to Buffalo for a vacation. Members of the general public could fly standby on the same flight for $100. A reserved-seat ticket costs $200. How much gross income must Francis recognize?

        (2)   Would your answer be different if Francis were allowed to purchase a reserved ticket for $175? For $100?

(b)   Agony Airlines allows officers and directors of the corporation to use small commuter planes and a pilot for their personal use, if a plane is not required for service that day. Vince Vicepres, his wife, and two children were the sole passengers on a flight to New York for the Thanksgiving Day parade. The flight was made at their request. Must Vince recognize gross income as a result of this trip? If so, how (in general terms) is the amount of income calculated?

(c)   (1)   Luxury Motors Sales Corp. sells and leases Mercedes-Benz automobiles. Sam Salesman is allowed to drive a new Mercedes for his personal use. Although there are no restrictions on Sam's right to use the car, other members of his family are not permitted to drive it. He uses the same car as a demonstrator during working hours. The model Sam drives sells for $40,000. How much gross income, if any, must Sam recognize from the use of the car?

        (2)   Would your answer be different if Sam were not allowed to drive the car out of town, to use the car on vacation, to store personal possessions in the car, or to drive the car more than 100 miles a week (outside of normal working hours)?

        (3)   Luxury Motors sold the Mercedes to Sam for $36,000. During the year, Luxury Motors sold 100 automobiles for an aggregate price of $4 million. It paid $3.5 million for those automobiles. How much gross income must Sam recognize?

(4)   What would be your answer to part (c)(3) if Luxury Motors had paid $3.7 million for the automobiles?

(d)   Hall Homes, Inc. builds and sells low-cost new homes (buildings, not double-wides). Dewey Cheetum, the leading salesman for Hall Homes, was allowed to purchase for $72,000 a new home that normally sells for $80,000. How much gross income must he recognize?

(e)   Megabucks Corp. provides an executive restaurant that serves lunches that cost the corporation an average of $8 to prepare and serve. Executives are charged only $2. How much gross income does an executive who eats lunch in the restaurant recognize? Would your answer be different if the restaurant were open to all white-collar employees, including clerks and secretaries?

(f)   (1)   Jox Sporting Goods offers employees a 10 percent discount on all items purchased from the store. Jox does not sell boats but has arranged for Moby Dick Boat Co. to give Jox employees a 5 percent discount on any boat purchased from Moby Dick. Steve Sweatsox, an employee of Jox, purchased a $10,000 boat from Moby Dick for $9,500. How much gross income must Steve recognize?

    (2)   What if Moby Dick, for reasons of its own and without any consultation with Jox, decided to offer the same 5 percent discount to Jox employees?

(g)   (1)   Jox also operates a gym (in a separate building) that is open to the general public. All Jox employees are entitled to free membership. A membership usually costs an individual $200 per year. How much gross income must a Jox employee who uses the gym recognize?

    (2)   Would your answer be different if the gym were not open to the general public?

(h)   (1)   Megabucks Corp. pays half of the annual dues to the Jox Gym for any employee who wants to join. Larry Lineworker joined the gym, and Megabucks paid Jox $100 of the $200 fee. How much gross income must Larry recognize?

    (2)   Domestic Pleasure Machines Corp. built a gym adjacent to its

factory. It costs Domestic about $100 per year per employee to operate the gym. How much income must an employee who uses the gym recognize?

(i) (1) Mega Corp. is headquartered in downtown Washington, D.C. For years it has provided free parking for its top seventy-nine executives, with a designated space reserved for each executive. Until the enactment of IRC § 132(f) in 1993, this was treated as a tax-free fringe benefit. The fair market value of a reserved parking space in downtown Washington is $355. Under current law, is the value of the parking taxable to the executives?

(2) Suppose the executives are not happy with the result in part (i)(1) and want a way to keep their free parking without paying any tax. Research reveals that unreserved monthly parking in the same area sells for $175 per month. Mega Corp. continues to provide the same seventy-nine spaces to the same seventy-nine executives, but stops designating particular spaces for particular persons. Mega Corp. claims that the spaces are now worth only $175 per month. What are the tax consequences to the executives?

(j) (1) RIF Corp. has recently announced plans to terminate the employment of several dozen mid-level managers. It has offered these managers free "outplacement counseling services" to help them find similar jobs with other corporations. The fair market value of these services is $2,000 per manager. Do the managers who accept the offer have income as a result?

(2) What if the managers are given the choice of $2,000 of outplacement counseling services or $2,000 severance pay? Will the managers who choose the services be taxed?

(k) Pat, an associate attorney employed by a large law firm, often travels in connection with his job. Pat earns substantial frequent flier miles on these trips, and the firm allows him to keep the frequent flier awards. Last year Pat used his miles to fly to Hawaii for a vacation. Is the value of his frequent flier awards taxable to Pat?

PROBLEM SET 8-3

¶ 8.03 GROUP TERM LIFE INSURANCE; ¶ 8.05 QUALIFIED TUITION REDUCTIONS; ¶ 8.06 EDUCATIONAL ASSISTANCE PROGRAMS

(a)   (1)   The architecture partnership of Frank, Floyd & Wrong provides group term life insurance coverage of $75,000 for all of its staff members. The staff consists of three professional architects and partners (Frank, Floyd, and Wrong), three secretaries, and one receptionist. Are the premiums attributable to the insurance on the lives of Frank, Floyd, and Wrong excludable from their gross income?

          (2)   Would your answer be different if the business were operated as a corporation, instead of a partnership?

(b)   Wattsammatta U. has a program under which employees and their immediate families are entitled to free tuition under certain circumstances. Professor Fringe teaches at Wattsammatta U. Law School. Her daughter, a college sophomore, receives free tuition at the College of Hard Knocks, under a reciprocal arrangement with Wattsammatta U. Professor Fringe's husband, a third-year law student at Wattsammatta U., also receives free tuition. The university's free tuition program satisfies the nondiscrimination rules of IRC § 117(d)(3). Does Professor Fringe have any gross income as a result of the free tuition program?

PROBLEM SET 8-4

¶ 8.01 INTRODUCTION; ¶ 8.03 GROUP TERM LIFE INSURANCE; ¶ 8.04 DEPENDENT CARE ASSISTANCE; ¶ 8.11 EMPLOYEE-CHOSEN BENEFITS ("CAFETERIA PLANS")

(a)   Charles Closecorp, the majority shareholder and president of Smallbiz, Inc., recently attended a Chamber of Commerce meeting on employee fringe benefits. He is a bit confused about the type of benefits that may be included in a cafeteria plan and would like you to clarify the rules for him. He is even more confused regarding the reasons for allowing only certain fringe benefits to be included in a cafeteria plan, while taxing other fringe benefits that would be tax free if provided outside the plan. Can you help Charles understand the rules and their rationale?

(b)   Representative Pangloss, from the state of Utopia, has introduced legislation to repeal IRC §§ 79, 105, 106, 125, 129, and 132. Representative Ogallala from Kansaska, for whom you are the tax adviser, has asked you to analyze the merits of the proposal for him. In particular, he wants to know whether the proposed changes will enhance or detract from tax equity and economic efficiency and whether the resulting laws would be administrable.

(c)   (1)   Jim and Jane are a married couple, both of whom work full time. Their combined adjusted gross income is $60,000. Their marginal tax rate is 26 percent. They have a young daughter, for whose child care they expect to spend $3,000 during the year. Jim's employer has a dependent care assistance program, which Jim can participate in through a cafeteria plan. Would he be better off taking advantage of the IRC § 21 child care credit instead?

        (2)   What if they expect to spend $5,000 on child care for their daughter?

        (3)   Suppose they expect to spend $8,000 on child care for their daughter. Can they exclude $5,000 under IRC § 129 and claim a credit with respect to $3,000 under IRC § 21?

PROBLEM SET 8-5

¶ 8.08 MEALS AND LODGING FURNISHED TO EMPLOYEES FOR CONVENIENCE OF THE EMPLOYER; ¶ 8.09 HOMES AND RENTAL ALLOWANCES FURNISHED TO MINISTERS

(a)   Millicent Moneybags employs a cook and two maids at her residence. She pays each employee $10,000, provides each with a two-room efficiency apartment within her house, and pays directly to the grocery store any amounts that they charge (up to $60 per week). Each employee must agree to live in the apartment in order to be employed. Normal working hours fall generally between 7:00 a.m. and 6:00 p.m., although the employees may be required to work evenings, sometimes unexpectedly, when Millicent has guests or gives parties. Are the maids' and cook's meals and lodgings excludable from their incomes under IRC § 119?

(b)   (1)   Toxic Chemical Corp. built a manufacturing facility 40 miles from the nearest inhabited community, from which all of its workers commute on a daily basis. Toxic Chemical Corp. prohibits employees from bringing lunch boxes and thermos bottles to work because of the danger of chemical contamination being carried out of the plant, although bag lunches and disposable beverage containers may be brought into the plant. To compensate for restrictions on lunch boxes, Toxic provides a company cafeteria at which meals are sold at 25 percent of Toxic's cost (which Toxic estimates to be equal to the cost that would be incurred by an employee who brought his lunch). Are the meals provided in the Toxic cafeteria excluded from an employee's income under IRC § 119? If the value of these meals is includable, how will Toxic compute the amount to be reported as includable by each employee?

        (2)   Would the result be different if Toxic charged nothing for the lunches?

(c)   (1)   Rabbi Ben Ezra receives a $10,000 "parsonage allowance" from the synagogue that employs him. He uses the allowance to make the mortgage payments on his house. Is he entitled to exclude the allowance from income?

        (2)   Of the $10,000 parsonage allowance, the Rabbi uses $8,000 to pay interest on his home mortgage. May he both exclude the $8,000 under IRC § 107 and deduct it under IRC § 163?

(d)   Reverend Sunday receives $100,000 from the church that employs him, designated as a parsonage allowance. He uses the $100,000 as a down payment on his new home. May he exclude the full amount under IRC § 107? The new house's annual rental value is $24,000.

9

Miscellaneous Items

PROBLEM SET 9-1

¶ 9.02 SOCIAL SECURITY BENEFITS

(a)   Anne is a single, retired person, living on a fully taxable pension of $18,000 a year, and Social Security benefits of $14,000 a year. She is considering taking a part time job, which would pay $8,000. If she does so, what will be the effect on her gross income? Assuming her statutory marginal tax rate under IRC § 1(c) is 15 percent, what is the real marginal tax rate on the $8,000 of earned income?

PROBLEM SET 9-2

¶ 9.06 EXCLUSION FOR SMALL BUSINESS STOCK

(a)   Jane, who is not married, bought 1,000 shares of Micro Corp. six years ago for $500,000. This year she sold all her shares for $15 million. If all of the requirements for the application of IRC § 1202 are satisfied, how much gain may Jane exclude from income?

(b)   (1)   In 1995, Moonbeam Coffee Co. sold newly issued shares in a private offering. Moonbeam satisfied the statutory definition of a "qualified small business" at the time. Moonbeam sold gourmet coffee beans, and coffee-related products, through retail stores and by mail order. Pursuant to the private offering, Georges paid $500,000 cash for 500 shares, and Gloria paid $1.2 million for 1,200 shares. Moonbeam did very well over the next few years. In 2004, Georges sold all his shares for $8 million, and Gloria sold all her shares for $19.2 million. How much gain must each of them include in income?

(2)   Assume the same facts as in part (b)(1), except that in 1997, Moonbeam expanded into the business of selling espresso

drinks for on- and off-premises consumption, and by 2000, the espresso drink business represented 30 percent of Moonbeam's total assets (by value). How much gain must Georges and Gloria include in income in that case?

PROBLEM SET 9-3

¶ 9.08 SALE OF PRINCIPAL RESIDENCE

(a)   Fiona (an unmarried taxpayer) purchased her house—the first house she had ever owned—for $200,000 on January 1 of this year, and moved in immediately. A few months later, a corporation in a distant city made her a job offer she couldn't refuse. She accepted the offer and put her house up for sale. On September 30 of this year she sold her house for $260,000. How much of her gain, if any, may she exclude under IRC § 121?

(b)   Larry and Lois, a married couple, bought their house many years ago for $200,000. Today it would sell for about $650,000. They know this because a very similar house across the street has just been placed on the market, with an asking price of $650,000. They expect houses in their neighborhood to continue to appreciate. Their house is debt-free (they paid off their mortgage years ago). They are considering taking out a $200,000 home equity loan to finance their children's college educations. Is there any tax reason why they might consider selling their house and buying the one across the street?

(c)   The current version of IRC § 121 replaced former IRC § 1034, which allowed a taxpayer to "rollover" gain on the sale of a principal residence by reinvesting the amount realized in a replacement residence. The mechanics of the provision closely resembled those of current IRC § 1033 (relating to gains on involuntary conversions). Section 1034 was merely a deferral provision, whereas IRC § 121 provides for the permanent exclusion of gain. Does it follow that all sellers of appreciated residences fare better under IRC § 121 than they would have under IRC § 1034?

(d)   Congress clearly intended IRC § 121 to exempt gain due to appreciation in residential real estate markets. Is there any way that a clever taxpayer could use IRC § 121 to obtain an exemption for *labor* income? Hint: It will help if the taxpayer is handy with tools and doesn't mind living with a little sawdust.

10

Interest on State and Local Obligations

PROBLEM SET 10-1

¶ 10.01 IN GENERAL

(a)   Fred Farmer sold his farm for $1 million to the state of California, which planned to establish a park on the land. The state paid Fred $100,000 in cash and gave him a promissory note for $900,000, due in ten years, bearing interest at 10 percent per year, due in each year. Under IRC § 103, may Fred exclude from his gross income the $90,000 of interest that he receives each year from the state?

(b)   Fred also recently received $1,000 in interest on a state income tax refund. May he exclude that $1,000 from his gross income under IRC § 103?

(c)   As a member of the Staff of the Joint Committee on Taxation, you have been asked to prepare a report for use in conjunction with hearings on a proposed bill to repeal IRC § 103. You have been asked specifically to analyze whether the repeal would enhance or reduce tax equity (fairness) and economic efficiency, as well as whether the repeal of IRC § 103 would be constitutional.

11

Expenses Incurred in Business and Profit-Oriented Activities

PROBLEM SET 11-1

¶ 11.01 INTRODUCTION

(a)   Billy Bassbuster owns and operates a successful fuel oil distributorship to which he devotes about 200 days a year. Billy spends the balance of the year chasing the elusive lunker bass in competitive fishing tournaments. Over the past five years, Billy has earned prizes totaling $60,000. Five years ago, Billy spent $20,000 for a boat, motor, and trailer, and another $20,000 for a pickup truck to tow the boat to the tournaments. Each year Billy spends almost $5,000 on equipment, supplies, gasoline, and tournament entry fees. Is Billy engaged in a trade or business, an activity for the production of income, or a hobby? Does it matter?

(b)   Sylvester Salesman sells commercial scales to wholesalers as a commission agent of the scale manufacturers. To increase sales, Sylvester told Wally Wholesaler that if Wally hired an additional wholesale salesman, Sylvester would reimburse Wally for 75 percent of the salesman's salary. May Sylvester deduct as an ordinary and necessary business expense the portion of Wally's employee's salary that Sylvester pays?

(c)   Linda Lawyer, an associate attorney employed by a large law firm, spent a week out of town trying a case. The firm's policy was to reimburse associates for all reasonable lodging expenses on business trips. Linda spent $100 per day for her hotel room, which was clearly reasonable. She decided not to request reimbursement, however, because she was up for partnership review in a few months, and the partners seemed to favor associates who really knew how to pinch a penny. She told the firm's business manager she had no lodging expenses for the trip, because she had stayed with a friend. May Linda deduct the lodging cost on her own return, as an employee business expense?

PROBLEM SET 11-2

¶ 11.02 THE BUSINESS-PERSONAL BORDERLINE

(a)   Representative Peter Pol has introduced legislation to allow deductions for (1) expenses of commuting to and from work and (2) child care expenses incurred by working parents for children under 13 years of age (or handicapped children without regard to age). If this legislation is enacted, will it create a deduction for an expense that is a personal expense or will it recognize a business expense for which a deduction is not currently allowed?

(b)   Jack Jox, a professional football player, spends $1,000 a year on vitamin supplements and high-protein additives to maintain his weight and strength, which are necessary to play defensive tackle. May Jack deduct the $1,000 as an ordinary and necessary business expense?

PROBLEM SET 11-3

¶ 11.03 THE "ORDINARY AND NECESSARY" QUALIFICATION ON THE DEDUCTIBILITY OF BUSINESS AND PROFIT-ORIENTED EXPENSES; ¶ 11.04 ILLEGAL PAYMENTS, BRIBES, FINES, ETC.; ¶ 11.05 LOBBYING AND OTHER LEGISLATIVE ACTIVITIES

(a)   Karl Kole, who owns a coal mine, paid a $10,000 bribe to a vice-president of Monolith Steel Corp. to influence the award of a contract to Karl's company to supply coal to Monolith for the next two years. May Karl deduct the bribe as an ordinary and necessary business expense?

(b)   Country singer Johnny "Pig" Wilson decided to form a restaurant chain featuring barbecued pork, called Pig's Pit. The business was incorporated as Pig's Pit, Inc. Much of the financing came from loans to the corporation from friends of Johnny. Because Johnny was an extremely popular entertainer, who had numerous Number 1 hits, the advertising campaign for the business featured Johnny extensively. Despite the campaign, the business failed, and the corporation was unable to repay its loans. Johnny, however, paid off all of the loans in full, even though he was under no legal obligation to do so. Johnny deducted the total amount repaid (about $200,000) under IRC § 162(a) as an expense of his business as a singer. (His annual income from singing was ordinarily between $1 million and $2 million.) Was the deduction proper?

(c)   The City Council of Springfield is considering a proposal to ban cigarette vending machines in any restaurant or other establishment open to persons under the age of 18. Merchants of Death Vending, Inc., is concerned that this would seriously cut into its profits. The company adopts a two-part strategy: (1) lobby the members of the City Council not to pass the measure and (2) lobby the state legislature to enact a law depriving local governments of all power to regulate with respect to cigarette sales. It spends $10,000 on each lobbying effort. Is the money deductible?

(d)   Home-Sweet-Home Corp. is the largest residential real estate brokerage in the country. When Congress was considering lowering the limitation of IRC § 163(h)(3) from $1 million to $200,000, Home-Sweet-Home Corp. spent hundreds of thousands of dollars lobbying (unsuccessfully) against the proposal, because it feared enactment of the proposal would dampen home sales. After the legislation was enacted, it spent additional tens of thousands of dollars trying to convince officials of the Treasury Department and the IRS to make the interpretive regulations as taxpayer-friendly as possible. Are these expenses deductible?

PROBLEM SET 11-4

¶ 11.08 NONBUSINESS PROFIT-ORIENTED ACTIVITIES OF INDIVIDUALS

(a)   Mary Money inherited from her late Uncle Rich $1 million in cash, which she initially deposited in a savings account at Trustworthy Savings & Loan Association. Mary consulted an investment adviser, because she was unfamiliar with the stock market but wanted to invest her money. The investment adviser charged Mary $2,000 to design a balanced portfolio that invested her inheritance in a variety of stocks. To purchase the stocks, Mary paid a stockbroker purchase commissions that totaled $10,000. The next year, Mary paid the investment adviser another $2,000 to reevaluate her portfolio. Pursuant to his advice, Mary sold some of the stock, paying sales commissions of $5,000. May Mary deduct any of these expenses under IRC § 212? How should the nondeductible expenses, if any, be treated?

(b)   A few years ago, Wally Woods purchased 100 acres of undeveloped land on the outskirts of Sun City, anticipating that the land would become more valuable as the city grew. Last year, after a subdivision was built nearby, Wally erected a six-foot-high chain link fence around a pond on his land at a cost of $10,000. He did this to prevent neighboring children from playing and possibly drowning in the pond and to protect himself from the resulting lawsuit. This year Wally paid $300 to repair a hole that had been cut in the fence by children who wanted to fish and swim in the pond. He also paid $2,000 to drain and fill a swampy area that presented a danger to children and bred mosquitos. May Wally deduct these various expenses under IRC § 212?

(c)   Edith Edger has owned a vacation home on Martha's Vineyard for over twenty years. Last year, Edith moved to San Diego and put the vacation home up for sale. Edith pays a realtor $1,000 a year to check the house weekly for security purposes, cut the lawn, clean up debris, and generally keep the house presentable for viewing by potential purchasers. May Edith deduct the fee paid to the realtor?

(d)   When Ralph and Ruth Roamer were divorced last year in a no-fault divorce proceeding, the only controversy involved the property settlement. Ruth sought a lump-sum cash settlement of $500,000. Ralph resisted on the grounds that he would be forced to sell several of his real estate investment properties. After protracted negotiation, Ralph finally agreed to pay Ruth $900,000 in ten annual installments of $90,000. The total sum payable was increased because the payments were deferred. Under the agreement, the $90,000 per year was taxable to Ruth, while the lump-sum payment would not have been taxable to her. Ruth paid her attorney $20,000 in conjunction with the property settlement negotiations, and Ralph paid his attorney $25,000. May Ralph and Ruth deduct their attorney fees?

(e)   Physicians Phantastic Phlyaway, Inc. (PPP), promotes week-long continuing medical education seminars held at a variety of locations in Hawaii. In conjunction with each medical seminar, PPP offers a coordinate seminar for the physicians' spouses on "Tax Planning for the Physician's Family." These seminars meet for four hours a day for five days. Felicity Physician and her husband Fred went to one of the PPP seminar weeks. Felicity attended the medical seminars, while Fred attended the twenty hours of tax seminars. The cost of Fred's seminar was $200; his plane ticket was $600; his hotel room was $700; and meals were $350. To what extent may Fred deduct these expenses under IRC § 212(3)? (See also ¶ 13.1.)

(f)   Wally Woods (from part (b)) has received an offer from Danny Developer, who wants to purchase the 100 acres of undeveloped land Wally owns near Sun City. Danny offered to pay Wally either (1) $1 million this year or (2) $100,000 this year and $1.4 million in installments as the houses he plans to build on the land are sold. Wally paid $2,000 to Tommy Taxes, his accountant, for advice regarding the tax consequences of the alternative proposals. How should Wally treat the $2,000 paid for tax advice?

PROBLEM SET 11-5

¶ 11.06 COMPENSATION FOR PERSONAL SERVICES

(a)   Gene Gizmo is the president and sole shareholder of Bassamatic Corp., which manufactures food processors specially designed for seafood recipes. Bassamatic was founded five years ago by Gene and his friend Charley Tuna. Gene and Charley each owned half of the stock of the corporation. Gene's original employment contract provided that he would receive a salary of $100,000 per year and a bonus equal to 10 percent of gross sales or 25 percent of profits, whichever was less. Charley, who was vice-president, had a similar contract. Charley died last year, and Gene purchased his stock in Bassamatic from Charley's widow. Gene then caused Bassamatic to give him a new contract at a salary of $200,000 per year, with a bonus equal to 20 percent of gross sales or 50 percent of profits, whichever was less. For the last five years the business has been fairly consistent. Sales have been $2 million and profits about $300,000, annually. No dividends have been paid. In an audit, the IRS has disallowed Bassamatic's deduction for Gene's compensation in excess of $100,000 for last year, the first year of his $200,000 salary and increased bonus. What arguments can you make on behalf of the corporation in support of the deduction? How should Gene and Bassamatic Corp. treat the compensation in excess of $100,000 if the IRS prevails?

(b)   Bassamatic Corp. also paid Gene's daughter, Ginger, $25,000 to be the southern California sales manager for Bassamatic. Ginger, who is a junior at the University of California at Laguna Beach, spent two nights a week (a total of eight hours a week) demonstrating Bassamatic food processors in supermarkets. Bassamatic had gross sales in California last year of $10,000. The IRS has disallowed Bassamatic's deduction of Ginger's salary in excess of $2,000. How should Ginger treat the excess $23,000?

(c)   Ellen Exec is the CEO of International Computer Manufacturers (ICM), a publicly held corporation. Her employment contract includes a yearly salary of $950,000 with a bonus of $950,000 if sales for the company at least maintain the status quo. Victor VP is the next highest paid officer. He has a similar contract calling for a yearly salary of $750,000 with a bonus of $750,000 if sales at least maintain the status quo. Sales for last year were over $2 billion and have been rising every year for the past ten years. As expected, sales rose again this year and both Ellen and Victor received their bonuses. May ICM deduct the full amount of compensation paid to Ellen and Victor?

(d)   Sam Sales, ICM's top dog sales person, handles many of the major corporate accounts. His employment contract calls for a base salary of $350,000, plus a percentage of his sales for commission. Sam's sales for this past year exceeded all expectations, and his commissions came to $900,000. May ICM deduct all compensation paid to Sam?

(e)   Assuming IRC § 162(m) actually results in the disallowance of some deductions in the real world, how should the provision's effect be reflected in the tax expenditure budget?

PROBLEM SET 11-6

¶ 11.07 RENTAL PAYMENTS

(a)   The medical professional association of Harte, Livers & Braine, PSC, leases office space in the Medical Arts Building, which is owned by Medical Arts Realty Associates, a partnership, all of the partners of which are the minor children of Drs. Harte, Livers, and Braine, but which is managed by the three doctors acting in their capacity as guardians of their children. The doctors, acting as managers of the partnership, have decided to raise rents in the building by $2 a square foot when leases come up for renewal. However, they propose to raise the rent for Harte, Livers & Braine, PSC, by $4 a square foot. They want to know if their medical professional association will be allowed to deduct the increased rent.

(b)   Sam Shrub leased five acres of land, on which there was a small building, from Lynn Landlord for the purpose of operating a retail nursery. The five-year lease required Sam to pay a monthly rent of $500 ($6,000 per year). Concurrently with the execution of the lease, Lynn gave Sam an option to buy the property at any time during the term of the lease. The price was $100,000 in the first year, but increased by $5,000 in each subsequent year. If Sam exercised the option, 50 percent of his previously paid rent (i.e., $3,000 per year) would be credited against the purchase price. To what extent may Sam deduct his monthly $500 rent payments?

12

Capital Expenditures

PROBLEM SET 12-1

¶ 12.01 INTRODUCTION; ¶ 12.02 EXPENDITURES TO ACQUIRE, CLEAR TITLE TO, AND DISPOSE OF PROPERTY; ¶ 12.03 BENEFIT EXTENDING SUBSTANTIALLY BEYOND THE TAXABLE YEAR; ¶ 12.04 EXPENDITURES TO INVESTIGATE, START, ENTER, OR EXPAND A BUSINESS

(a) Sulphuric Electric Power Corp. is a large Midwestern public utility serving the southern half of the state of Indihio. Historically, all of Sulphuric's power plants were coal-fired. Ten years ago, Sulphuric began studying patterns for electricity demand in Indihio and the adjacent state of Kentuckiana. Based on this study, which cost $100,000, Sulphuric decided to expand into the Kentuckiana market. In addition, Sulphuric spent $50,000 for legal, accounting, and engineering fees in connection with a Public Service Commission hearing to obtain the right to provide electric power in Kentuckiana. After receiving a franchise to serve forty counties in Kentuckiana, Sulphuric made the following expenditures in connection with the construction of a new nuclear power plant in Kentuckiana:

1.	Land acquisition	$ 1,000,000
2.	Legal fees for land acquisition	$ 10,000
3.	Engineering and legal fees for environmental impact study and Nuclear Regulatory Commission permit	$ 500,000
4.	Construction of power plant	$10,000,000

A salaried employee of Sulphuric's in-house engineering department supervised construction over a ten-year period. Her aggregate salary for that period was $600,000. Sulphuric also expended $1 million above its normal advertising budget to emphasize the safety of nuclear power plants. Finally, in the year before the actual operation of the new nuclear plant began, Sulphuric spent $800,000 in salary and training costs to instruct new employees and to retrain employees transferred from coal-fired plants to nuclear power facilities. Sulphuric obtained the funds for this project by selling 1.6 million shares of new common stock to the public, a transaction for which it paid E.F. Lynch, the underwriter, $1 million in fees. To what extent are the various expenses Sulphuric incurred in expanding its operations into Kentuckiana deductible under IRC § 162?

(b)   (1)   Joseph Carpenter is a maker of fine handcrafted furniture. Each piece he makes is unique. He and his customers consider his furniture to be works of art, although they are also completely functional as furniture. Last year he completed twelve pieces, spending a month on each. He sold five of those pieces last year. The other seven were still in his inventory at the end of the year. He paid $500 per month rent for his workshop and paid $75 per month for utilities for the workshop. May Joseph currently deduct his expenses for rent and utilities?

         (2)   Wilhelm Schlockmeister paints pictures on black velvet. His specialty is children with very large eyes, although he also does his share of kittens, puppies, Elvises, and Last Suppers. Last year, he completed twelve pieces, spending a month on each (amazingly enough). He sold five of the paintings last year. The other seven were still in his inventory at the end of the year. He paid $500 per month in rent for his studio and paid $75 per month for utilities for the studio. May Wilhelm currently deduct his expenses for rent and utilities?

(c)   Blighted Real Estate Corp. is in the business of operating low-rent apartment buildings. Last year, Blighted sold a building that it no longer wanted to Slumlord Corp. The terms of the sale were $100,000 cash at the closing and $300,000 to be paid one year later. When the $300,000 payment came due, Slumlord paid only $250,000, claiming a right to offset the other $50,000 because of latent defects in the building at the time of sale. Blighted sued Slumlord for the $50,000 and won. Blighted's attorney retained $15,000 of the judgment as his fee. May Blighted deduct the $15,000 fee under IRC § 162?

50

PROBLEM SET 12-2

¶ 12.01 INTRODUCTION; ¶ 12.02 EXPENDITURES TO ACQUIRE, CLEAR TITLE TO, AND DISPOSE OF PROPERTY; ¶ 12.03 BENEFIT EXTENDING SUBSTANTIALLY BEYOND THE TAXABLE YEAR; ¶ 12.05 REPAIRS VERSUS IMPROVEMENTS AND REPLACEMENTS

(a)   To control emissions of sulphuric acid at its coal-fired generating plants, Sulphuric Electric Power Corp., at a cost of $5 million, installed scrubbers that chemically remove the sulphuric acid from the smoke. When installed ten years ago, the scrubbers had an expected useful life of twenty years, and the expected life of the generating facility, which cost $25 million, was over forty years.

      (1)   The Environmental Protection Agency (EPA) has recently eased emission standards. To cut the costs of operating the scrubbers, Sulphuric constructed (at a cost of $500,000) a system that permits smoke to bypass the scrubbers and to enter the stack directly. Must Sulphuric capitalize the $500,000 or may it deduct the expense?

      (2)   The EPA has once again toughened emission standards. It is now necessary for Sulphuric to spend $500,000 to remove a previously installed mechanism that permitted the smoke to bypass the scrubbers. May Sulphuric deduct this expense?

(b)   As part of a preventive maintenance program, the Atlantic and Pacific Railroad Corp. overhauls the diesel motors of its locomotives every two years, at a cost of $500,000 per locomotive. A new locomotive that costs $5 million is typically used for twenty years prior to being replaced, and its two motors are typically replaced at the end of the first ten years. This year, when overhauling Engine No. 9, the maintenance crew replaced one of the two diesel motors at a cost of $1.5 million, although the locomotive was only four years old. This was done because it was more cost-efficient than to separately repair the unusual number of problems. May the A&P deduct the cost of the new diesel motor?

(c)   Mega Corp. owns a building that it has used in its business many years—so long, in fact, that the adjusted basis is zero. The building was damaged in a recent earthquake. The fair market value of the building, immediately before the earthquake, was $1 million. The earthquake damage reduced the value to $800,000. After $200,000 worth of structural repairs (which were not covered by insurance), the value was again $1 million. Does it make any difference whether Mega Corp. (1) deducts the $200,000 cost of the repair or (2) deducts the $200,000 damage as a casualty loss and capitalizes the repair?

(d)   Dioxin Corp. has operated a manufacturing plant in a particular location for more than two decades. Those operations have caused groundwater contamination, which state and federal regulations now require Dioxin to alleviate. Dioxin has found there are two methods of complying with the environmental law requirements. The first method requires construction of groundwater treatment facilities, which will remain in operation on Dioxin's land for twelve years. The second method involves intensive groundwater treatment during the current year, without the construction of any permanent facilities. Each method will cost the same amount, and aside from possible tax differences Dioxin has no preference between them. Which method should Dioxin choose? (Dioxin has changed its operating methods, so it will cause no groundwater contamination in the future. Thus, either method will deal with only the effects of past operations.)

PROBLEM SET 12-3

¶ 12.04 EXPENDITURES TO INVESTIGATE, START, ENTER, OR EXPAND A BUSINESS; ¶ 12.06 EXPENDITURES TO CREATE OR PRESERVE TAXPAYER'S BUSINESS REPUTATION

(a)   Lucy Lawstudent and her brother Larry Lawstudent are both in their last year at Legendary Law School. Last summer, they both clerked with large Wall Street law firms. Lucy, who has chosen to practice corporate law, accepted a permanent job with a large Wall Street firm. During the interview season, she made five separate trips to New York, and all of her expenses (in the aggregate amount of $5,000) were paid by the interviewing firms. Her brother Larry decided he wanted to be a small-town lawyer in northern New England and spent nearly $1,500 of his own money to travel to interviews with small law firms that could not pay his expenses. What are the separate income tax consequences for Larry and Lucy, both of whom ultimately obtained jobs?

(b)   Since she graduated from law school four years ago, Jane Jurist has been an associate with a large firm, specializing in federal tax law. During the past year, she has also taught two income tax classes as an adjunct professor at Local Law School. She recently decided to become a full-time law professor. Her successful search for a full-time teaching job cost her $1,500 in travel expenses. Are those expenses deductible under IRC § 162?

(c)   In INDOPCO, Inc. v. CIR, 503 US 79, 87 (1992), the Supreme Court stated that "a taxpayer's realization of benefits beyond the year in which the expenditure is incurred is undeniably important in determining whether the appropriate tax treatment is immediate deduction or capitalization." Prior to *INDOPCO*, businesses had been allowed current deductions for virtually all advertising expenses, even where the advertising was designed to produce benefits beyond the current year. Does *INDOPCO* call into question the deductibility of some kinds of advertising, such as goodwill advertising (e.g., television advertisements for Boeing, apparently intended to make people feel good about air travel), and advertising of new product lines (e.g., the first year's advertising for Saturn, Lexus, and Infiniti cars)?

13

Mixed Purpose Expenditures—
Business or Profit-Oriented Expense
Versus Personal Expense

PROBLEM SET 13-1

¶ 13.01 TRAVEL AND TRANSPORTATION; ¶ 13.02 COMBINED BUSINESS-PLEASURE TRAVEL

(a)   Donna Domestic lives in an apartment in a lower-middle-class neighborhood of the city of Los Diego. It costs her $2 for bus fare every day to commute to her job. She is a maid for Mrs. Moneybags, who lives in an upper-class neighborhood of Los Diego called El Camino Del Rey Mar Vista. She is paid the minimum wage. May Donna deduct the bus fare?

(b)   (1)   Barry Barrister lives in Laguna Hills and maintains a law office about two miles from his home. Barry spends about 50 percent of his time in his office and 50 percent of his time in court or taking depositions elsewhere. May Barry deduct his expenses of driving his Mercedes-Benz from his office to the court and back again? May he deduct parking fees at the court?

       (2)   If Barry drives directly from his home to the court, from the court to his office, and then from the office to his home, what portion of his transportation is deductible?

       (3)   (i)   If Barry drives from his home to the airport, from which he flies to Los Francisco to take a deposition, and returns on a flight that same evening, may Barry deduct his airfare? May he deduct the cost of driving to and from the airport? May he deduct the cost of his lunch while in Los Francisco?

              (ii)   If Barry stays overnight in Los Francisco, may he deduct the cost of his lunch, dinner, and breakfast?

(c)   Vera Viola is employed as a member of the New York Philharmonic. Because of inadequate individual rehearsal room at Lincoln Center, she does most of her practicing in her apartment in a room set aside for that purpose. Assuming she qualifies for a home office deduction under IRC § 280A, because her home is her principal place of business, may she deduct the cost of cab fare between her apartment and Lincoln Center for group rehearsals and performances?

(d)   (1)   Barry Barrister was invited to be a Distinguished Visiting Professor of Trial Skills at Ivy Law School for the academic year. Barry rented his house in Laguna Hills to a former classmate who was serving that same year as a visiting professor at the University of Laguna Hills. He then rented a home in Ivytown to live in (with his wife and two children) for the academic year. To what extent may Barry deduct his rent in Ivytown, his groceries and restaurant expenses in Ivytown, and the cost of traveling between Ivytown and Laguna Hills?

    (2)   If Ivy Law School gave Barry the option of teaching for either an academic year (September to June) or a calendar year, is there any tax reason for Barry to prefer one option over the other?

    (3)   Suppose that after the visit has lasted for seven months, Barry and Ivy Law School are surprised at how much they like each other, and Barry accepts an offer of a tenured faculty position at the school. Would this change your answer to part (d)(1)?

    (4)   Suppose that the facts are the same as in part (d)(1), except the term of visit is three consecutive semesters, covering sixteen months. What expenses may Barry deduct in that case?

    (5)   At the close of the year that he served as a visiting professor at Ivy Law School, Barry was appointed Deputy Assistant Attorney General of the United States by the newly elected President of the United States. Barry's family returned to their home in Laguna Hills. Barry rented an apartment in the Watergate in Washington, D.C., and flew back to Laguna every other weekend to see his family and meet with his stockbroker. May Barry deduct his rent at the Watergate, his groceries and restaurant expenses in Washington, D.C., and the cost of traveling between Washington, D.C., and Laguna Hills?

(e)   Suzie Slalom works as a ski patrol member at a ski resort in Colorado from November to April. From May to October, Suzie works as a lifeguard in Florida. May Suzie deduct her living expenses in either Colorado or Florida? What factors will determine which location is Suzie's home?

(f)   Kathleen Kollegegrad lives with her husband in University City, where she attends State University Law School. Her husband teaches in the English department of State University. During her second year of law school, Kathleen worked twenty hours a week as a law clerk for a local law firm. During the summer between her second and third years, Kathleen worked for Big Law Firm, PSC, in Metropolis, about 200 miles away from University City, where she rented an apartment. May Kathleen deduct her living expenses in Metropolis?

(g)   Willie Loman is the ultimate traveling salesman. He has no permanent home. Instead, he is always "on the road," living out of a suitcase, sleeping at Motel 6s, and eating at Denny's Restaurants. Can he deduct his motel and food expenses under IRC § 162?

(h)   (1)   Lucy Lawyer attended the American Bar Association's (ABA's) annual meeting in Honolulu last year. Lucy left Chiapolis (where she practices law) on Saturday and arrived in Honolulu on Sunday morning to sightsee for three days before the meeting began on Wednesday. Lucy diligently attended the sessions for eight days (from Wednesday through the next Wednesday), until the meeting ended. Lucy left Oahu on Wednesday and spent a few days (Thursday through Sunday) relaxing on the big island of Hawaii before flying back to Chiapolis. To what extent are Lucy's airfare, hotel bills, and meals deductible?

(2)   What would be your answer if the ABA meeting were held in London, for which Lucy departed from Chiapolis by direct flight on Saturday before the Wednesday opening of the meeting, and from which she returned to Chiapolis by direct flight leaving London on the Sunday following the close of the meeting?

(i)   Paul, a partner in a large law firm, frequently travels out of town on business. In recent years, his wife, Diane, has always accompanied him on their trips. Diane is not an employee of Paul or of Paul's firm. Paul agreed to this arrangement after he found that his unaccompanied business trips tended to "degenerate into stag affairs, where the whole purpose . . . would be lost." Are Diane's travel expenses deductible?

PROBLEM SET 13-2

¶ 13.03 ENTERTAINMENT, AMUSEMENT, AND RECREATION; ¶ 13.05 SUBSTANTIATION

(a)   Andy Agent, a life insurance salesman, eats lunch every day at a restaurant with either a prospective client, a lawyer, or an accountant, and Andy always pays the check. Andy sometimes discusses the purchase of a life insurance policy with the prospective customer and sometimes does not, preferring the soft sell on some occasions. Andy's purpose in taking lawyers and accountants to lunch is to build up goodwill in hopes that they will refer potential customers to him. To what extent may Andy deduct the cost of the meals?

(b)   All eight partners of the law firm of Hamlet & MacBeth belong to the Country Club. The partners hold a partnership meeting at the Country Club over lunch three times a week to discuss the current status of legal matters being handled by the firm and the progress of associates. All the partners play golf, frequently with clients, and their spouses and children also use the golf and swimming facilities. To what extent may the partners deduct the cost of their lunches? To what extent may the partners deduct their country club dues?

(c)   (1)   Sam Salesman bought two tickets to the World Indoor Football Championship game for $40 each and used the tickets to attend the game with Benny Buyer, whom Sam was hoping would place a large order. Under which of the following circumstances may Sam deduct the cost of the tickets?
          (i)   Sam and Benny discussed no business before, at, or after the game.
          (ii)   Sam and Benny discussed business at half time.

> (iii)   Sam and Benny discussed business on the way to and from the game.
>
> (iv)   Sam and Benny discussed business at Sam's office the day before the game.
>
> (v)   Sam and Benny ate dinner before the game and discussed business at dinner.

(2)   How will the Commissioner of Internal Revenue know whether Sam and Benny discussed business?

(3)   How much may Sam deduct if he bought only one ticket that he gave to Benny, who went to the game alone?

(4)   Must Benny recognize gross income in any of the above situations?

(d)   (1)   While on a business trip for her employer, Anne Agent spent $500 on meals for herself. When she returned from the trip, she presented the meal receipts to her employer and received $500 reimbursement. What are the tax consequences of these events to Anne and her employer?

(2)   Luigi's Restaurant had expenses of $1 million last year, in connection with meals sold to customers. Does IRC § 274(n) apply to limit its deduction for those expenses to $500,000?

(e)   Bev Biz travels hundreds of thousands of miles on business every year. She could fly coach, and she could rest between flights in public areas of airports, but she chooses to fly first class and to rest between flights in airlines clubs. Although she sometimes watches television or has a drink at an airline club, she uses the clubs mostly to make business phone calls and work on her computer. May she deduct the excess cost of first class over coach? May she deduct her airline club dues?

PROBLEM SET 13-3

¶ 13.06 EDUCATIONAL EXPENSES AS BUSINESS EXPENSES

(a)   Eddie, Elmo, and Edith Engineer, who are triplets, all graduated from State University three years ago with bachelor's degrees in electrical engineering. Upon graduation, Eddie began working for Worldwide Recreational Machines Corp. as an engineer. After two years, Eddie took an unpaid leave of absence and returned to State University for a year to earn his master's degree in electrical engineering, after which he resumed his job at Worldwide. Elmo continued his education at State University, earning a master's degree in electrical engineering before taking a job with Dallas Instruments designing microchips. Edith worked as an electrical engineer for a year before quitting her job and returning to State University for two years to earn a master's degree in chemical engineering, after which she began work for Toxic Chemical Corp. To what extent may Eddie, Elmo, and Edith deduct their expenses for tuition, books, and room and board incurred in pursuit of their education?

(b)   Senator Wellheeled, a member of the Senate Finance Committee, has introduced a bill to amend the Code to allow a deduction for tuition for any undergraduate or graduate college program, to the extent that the tuition is in excess of what the individual would have paid if he had attended the land grant state university of his state of residence. The Senator believes that this will correct an existing inequity in the current treatment of education expenses. Is he correct?

(c)   Your neighbor, Ruth Resident, graduated from medical school two years ago. Her total expenses for tuition and books while in medical school were $120,000. On last year's tax return, Ruth deducted $2,000 as amortization of her capitalized medical education costs. She computed this sum by dividing her total expenses by her remaining actuarial life expectancy of sixty years. Ruth has been audited by the IRS, and the revenue agent has disallowed the deduction as a personal expense. Ruth has cornered you at a neighborhood cookout and wants to know how anyone can be so silly as to term the expenses of a medical education a personal rather than a business expense.

PROBLEM SET 13-4

¶ 13.08 MOVING EXPENSES

(a)   Tina Teacher had been teaching in the town of Suburbia for several years. She lived across the street from the school. Last year, Tina took a position as principal of a school in Big City. The new school is fifty-two miles from her home and old school in Suburbia. At the same time that she began work in Big City, she moved to a home in Resort City Beach, which is fifty-five miles from her job in Big City. She commutes to Big City each day. Is Tina eligible to deduct her moving expenses?

(b)   Why are individuals permitted to deduct moving expenses incurred with respect to the commencement of their first employment, but denied a deduction for the expenses of seeking that employment?

(c)   Ellie Exec, a vice-president of Sugar Cola Corp., was recently reassigned from the western sales office in San Francisco to the eastern sales office in New York. In connection with Ellie's move, Sugar Cola paid $3,000 for Ellie, her husband, and two children to go to New York for one week, on two separate occasions, to look for a new home; $1,000 airfare for Ellie and her family to fly to New York when they moved; $10,000 to move their household possessions; $1,000 for motel and restaurant bills incurred by Ellie's family while in New York pending the closing; and $4,000 in cash paid to Ellie for the "aggravation" of relocating. How should Ellie account for the payments by Sugar Cola Corp. and the expenses of moving when computing her income taxes?

PROBLEM SET 13-5

¶ 13.09 HOBBIES AND OTHER ACTIVITIES NOT ENGAGED IN FOR PROFIT

(a)   Chris Cowpens, a professor of animal science at State University, earns a yearly salary of $60,000. Six years ago, Chris paid $20,000 to buy a fifteen-acre farm with two dilapidated barns about twenty-five miles outside of University City. There is no house on the farm; Chris has continued to reside in University City but goes to his farm two or three evenings during the week and spends almost every weekend at the farm.

Over the years, Chris has lost more money than he has made from the farm. He continues farming for a number of reasons, however, including the educational experience he believes his children are receiving by helping around the farm. Chris raises cattle, usually purchasing feeder calves and selling them after fattening them on grass in the summer, and on grain for those few cattle he keeps through the winter. He also keeps four pleasure horses on the farm. Over the last six years, the earnings from the farm have been as follows:

Last year	($ 500)
2 years ago	($4,000)
3 years ago	$ 500
4 years ago	($1,500)
5 years ago	$ 200
6 years ago	($1,000)

At the beginning of almost every year, Chris believes that he can turn a profit, but a disaster usually occurs. Six years ago, several cattle died; four years ago, drought necessitated purchasing more feed than anticipated. Two years ago, both disasters struck concurrently, and when Chris received an offer from a developer to buy the farm for $50,000, he seriously considered it before ultimately rejecting it, because he wanted his sons to experience farm work.

The IRS has audited Chris' return for last year and proposes to disallow the loss incurred from his farm. Last year Chris claimed the following deductions: (1) $500 in real estate taxes; (2) $1,500 interest on the mortgage on the farm; (3) $2,000 for feed; (4) $1,000 of accelerated cost recovery system (ACRS) deductions on the barns, his tractor, and other equipment; (5) $1,000 for repairs to barns, fences, and equipment; and (6) $1,000 of miscellaneous expenses, including veterinarian bills, dues to the Beef Cattle Association, and publications regarding cattle farming. He realized gross receipts of $11,500 from the sale of his cattle that survived the summer; he had purchased the cattle for $5,000 that spring. The revenue agent proposes to allow only the real estate taxes as a deduction. To what extent should Chris be allowed to deduct his expenses?

(b) Would taxpayers with hobby losses pay more or less tax if IRC § 183 were repealed?

31 days personal used

PROBLEM SET 13-6

¶ 13.10 RESIDENTIAL PROPERTY USED FOR BUSINESS AND PROFIT-ORIENTED PURPOSES—HOME OFFICES AND VACATION HOMES

(a)   Carl and Candy Condo purchased a condominium unit on Hilton Head Island, South Carolina, for $660,000 last July 1. Carl and Candy stayed at the condominium from July 1 to July 20 for a vacation. From July 21 to September 30, the condominium was rented at fair market value. For most of this time the condominium was rented to strangers; however, from July 21 to July 31, Carl's sister Cathy rented the condominium at fair market value. From October 1 to October 30, Carl let the owner of the company for which he works use the condominium without charging any rent. Carl hoped to gain his boss's goodwill, which might lead to a promotion and raise. During November and December, the condominium was vacant. Carl and Candy received a total of $7,000 for renting out the condominium. They incurred the following out-of-pocket expenses: (1) realtor's commissions, $400; (2) mortgage interest, $3,000; (3) real estate taxes, $1,800; and (4) insurance and maintenance, $600. The ACRS for July through December would have been $12,000 if the condominium had been used solely for business. Carl and Candy have asked you how the items relating to the condominium should be reported on their income tax return. What is your advice?

personal use

personal use disallowed not used exempt from exempt

31
30
31
92 × 10

9

(b)   Peter Prof is an assistant professor of architecture at Ivy University. To obtain tenure, Peter must publish; otherwise, he will perish. Rather than publish articles in scholarly journals, Peter has embarked on a book on the influence of modern architecture on the city of Chicago. He not only expects the book to earn him tenure but he also expects to make a profit. Wriggley Publishing Corp. has advanced Peter $1,000 for rights to the book. In addition, he will receive a royalty of 15 percent of sales. Peter will write the book on his computer. Not wanting to leave his computer in his office at Ivy University, he has set aside one room of his three-room apartment as an "office" in which to research and write his book. May Peter deduct one third of his annual rent of $12,000 as a business expense?

(c)   Mary owns and lives in a nice, but not opulent, house in a city that will soon host the Olympic Games. Under normal circumstances, the house would rent for about $2,000 a month. During the Olympics, however, she could easily rent it out for $4,000 a week. Mary is not interested in the Olympics, and she would like to do some rent gouging and go on vacation, but she is concerned about the taxes she would have to pay on the rental income. Can you offer her any advice?

14

Depreciation and Amortization

PROBLEM SET 14-1

¶¶ 14.01–14.12 (THE ENTIRE CHAPTER)

Note: In all of these problems, assume IRC § 168(k) does not apply, unless otherwise stated.

(a)　(1)　Donna Ditto operates a photocopying business. She purchased a state-of-the-art copier on January 1, 2003, for $100,000. She expects to use the copier for ten years and then to sell it for $20,000. What will be the accelerated cost recovery system (ACRS) deductions allowable with respect to the copier, assuming that Donna does not elect to claim a deduction under IRC § 179? (Note: Copiers have a five-year ACRS recovery period. Rev. Proc. 87-56, 1987-2 CB 674, 676.)

　　　(2)　What would be the answer in part (a)(1) if Donna elected to expense $10,000 of the cost of the copier under IRC § 179?

　　　(3)　What would be the answer in part (a)(1) if IRC § 168(k) applied?

　　　(4)　What would be the answer to part (a)(1) if the copier cost $120,000 and Donna elected, pursuant to IRC § 168(g)(7), to use the alternative depreciation system with respect to the copier? (Note: the recovery period would be six years. Rev. Proc. 87-56, 1987-2 CB 674, 676.)

　　　(5)　What would be the answer to part (a)(1) if Donna sold the copier for $70,000 on December 31, 2005?

(b)　(1)　On March 1, 2003, Lenny Landlord purchased an apartment building for $3 million, of which $250,000 represented the price of the land. What will be Lenny's ACRS deductions in 2003, 2004 and 2005, assuming that he wants to maximize his current deductions?

(2)   What would be the answer to part (b)(1) if Lenny elects, pursuant to IRC § 168(g)(7), to use the alternative depreciation system?

(3)   Lenny expended $20,000 to plant oak trees around the building. They have an expected botanical life of at least seventy-five years. How should Lenny recover the cost of the oak trees?

(c)   Vera Viola, who plays first violin for the New York Philharmonic, purchased a 250-year-old Stradivarius violin for $130,000. Musical instruments have not been assigned a "class life." What is the ACRS recovery period for the Stradivarius?

PROBLEM SET 14-2

¶ 14.03 EFFECT OF DEPRECIATION ON BASIS; ¶ 14.04 ELIGIBLE PROPERTY

(a)   Tommy Tenant rented two contiguous parcels of undeveloped land. He leased one parcel for forty years, and he built a hardware store on it at a cost of $100,000. He leased the other parcel for ten years, and he erected a shed on it to store lumber for his lumberyard at a cost of $20,000. How should Tommy recover the cost of each building?

(b)   Carl Contractor purchased a backhoe for $50,000 on July 1. (IRC §§ 168(k) and 179 did not apply to the backhoe.) From July 1 to August 15, Carl used the backhoe to dig a foundation for his new personal residence, excavate a pool in the backyard, and dig a farm pond in front of his house. From August 16 to September 30, the backhoe was used in connection with the construction of a new headquarters building for Carl's Construction Company. From October 1 to December 31, the backhoe was used to dig foundations on several projects for which Carl had been hired as a subcontractor. What is the amount of Carl's ACRS deduction for the year of purchase of the backhoe? (Assume the backhoe has a five-year ACRS recovery period.) What is his basis in the backhoe as of January 1?

PROBLEM SET 14-3

¶ 14.04[5] ELIGIBLE PROPERTY, INTANGIBLE PROPERTY; ¶ 14.10 AMORTIZATION OF INTANGIBLES

(a)   Extragalactic Electronics Corp. purchased a patent for a new laser-based communications device for $10 million. The patent has eight years to run. How will Extragalactic recover the cost of the patent? Does it matter whether Extragalactic purchased the patent as part of a larger purchase of an entire business, or as an independent purchase?

(b)   Suppose a corporation purchases a mail-order business, and $1.5 million of the purchase price is allocated to a customer list. The customer list would decline in value by $100,000 a year, but for the fact that the corporation spends $100,000 annually on advertising to replace departing customers with new customers. At the end of fifteen years, the corporation has spent $1.5 million maintaining the list, and the list is still worth $1.5 million. How will the acquisition and maintenance costs of the list be treated for tax purposes, and how does that treatment compare with economic reality?

PROBLEM SET 14-4

¶ 14.11 DEDUCTION AND AMORTIZATION OF CAPITAL EXPENDITURES

(a)   If you were compiling a report detailing all of the tax expenditures that it would be administratively feasible to repeal, would IRC § 174 be on your list?

(b)   (1)   Sue Shutterbug decided to quit her job as an attorney in the Office of Chief Counsel of the IRS and open a camera shop. Sue spent a total of $3,000 for transportation, meals, and lodging on each of three trips to investigate retail camera shops that were for sale in three different towns ($1,000 per trip). Sue spent another $500 for legal and accounting fees to investigate the two shops that she did not ultimately acquire and another $1,000 in legal and accounting fees to purchase the business she selected. Immediately upon her purchase, Sue closed the shop for two weeks to reorganize the business. She spent $2,000 for transportation, meals, and lodging to visit two camera manufacturers' headquarters to discuss the designation of her shop as an authorized factory service center. She paid $1,000 in salaries to employees who took inventory, placed orders for equipment, and stocked the shelves for the grand opening. To what extent are these expenses currently deductible by Sue, and to what extent are the expenses that are not currently deductible amortizable under IRC § 195?

(2)   Would your answer be different if, instead of buying the assets and conducting the business as a sole proprietor, Sue bought all of the stock of a corporation that conducted the business?

PROBLEM SET 14-5

¶ 14.12 "LISTED PROPERTY"—AUTOMOBILES AND OTHER MEANS OF TRANSPORTATION, COMPUTERS AND CELLULAR TELEPHONES, ETC.

(a)   (1)   Sam Salesman purchased a new Mercedes-Benz automobile for $40,000 on July 1. Assuming that Sam uses the automobile solely for business, what will be his allowable ACRS deduction for the first year he owns the car?

(2)   Would your answer be different if the automobile (not a new Mercedes, obviously) cost $10,000?

(3)   Would your answer to part (a)(2) be different if 40 percent of Sam's mileage was for business and 60 percent for pleasure?

(4)   Would your answer to part (a)(1) be different if 40 percent of Sam's mileage was for business and 60 percent was for pleasure?

(b)   (1)   Lucy Lawyer, a partner in a small law firm, purchased a new Peaches II personal computer for $3,600 last year. She kept the computer in her study at home, and her records of hours of use show that 45 percent of its use was to prepare briefs and documents for her law practice; 15 percent was for analysis of her portfolio investments; and 40 percent was for personal use, such as balancing her checkbook and playing video games. To what extent may Lucy claim ACRS deductions with respect to the computer?

(2) What would be your answer if the personal computer had been purchased by Paula Prof, an untenured assistant professor at State University, who also kept it at home, but used the computer solely to research and write scholarly articles that she had to publish to gain tenure?

15

Depletion Allowance and Related Deductions

PROBLEM SET 15-1

¶ 15.01 DEPLETION: IN GENERAL; ¶ 15.02 COST DEPLETION; ¶ 15.03 PERCENTAGE DEPLETION; ¶ 15.04 PRODUCTION PAYMENTS

(a)   Fred Farmer discovered a large sand and gravel deposit on a farm he owned. Fred granted Carl Contractor the right to extract as much sand and gravel as he wanted in exchange for $1,000 in cash and $1 for every ton extracted. In one year, Carl extracted 50,000 tons of gravel, which was 50 percent of the estimated deposit, paid Fred $50,000, and sold the gravel to Ricky Roadbuilder for $150,000. Carl incurred expenses of $50,000 to extract the gravel. What is the depletion deduction allowable for Fred and Carl?

(b)   What is the purpose of cost depletion? What is the purpose of percentage depletion? Why is percentage depletion allowed as an alternative to cost depletion, rather than in addition to cost depletion?

PROBLEM SET 15-2

¶ 15.05 INTANGIBLE DRILLING AND DEVELOPMENT COSTS; ¶ 15.06 EXPLORATION AND DEVELOPMENT EXPENDITURES

(a)   Representative Soapbox has introduced legislation to repeal IRC § 263(c) and specifically to require that the costs of drilling oil and gas wells be capitalized, with the cost recovered over the life of the well. Theoretically, would this treatment be more proper than the current treatment? Unless IRC § 616 were similarly repealed, would coal gain a competitive economic advantage over oil as an alternative fuel?

16

Loss Transactions

PROBLEM SET 16-1

¶ 16.01 INTRODUCTION; ¶ 16.02 RELATION TO BUSINESS AND PROFIT-ORIENTED TRANSACTIONS

(a)   Last year, Ruth Realtor sold three houses that she owned. The first house, her personal residence, had a basis of $80,000, and she received $90,000 when she sold it. The second house, her vacation home, had a basis of $50,000 and sold for $45,000. The third house, a duplex that she rented out, had a basis of $100,000 and sold for $95,000. To what extent are Ruth's economic losses on the vacation home and the duplex deductible in computing taxable income?

(b)   Ruth Realtor had a second vacation home in Florida, in which she had a basis of $50,000. On January 1, she was offered $45,000 by a prospective purchaser. Ruth agreed to sell, but the deal fell through when the purchaser went bankrupt. Ruth then decided to rent the house, instead of selling it. She first rented it on February 1, and continued to rent it until she sold it several years later for $32,000. During the time she rented the house, she properly claimed $10,000 of depreciation deductions with respect to it. What, if anything, is Ruth's deductible loss on the sale of the house?

(c)   Val Vet purchased an airplane for $20,000. (Val did not expense any of the cost under IRC § 179, and IRC § 168(k) did not apply.) Sixty percent of Val's use of the plane was business use (flying to remote farms to treat sick animals), and 40 percent was pleasure use. During the period Val owned the plane, Val properly claimed accelerated cost recovery system deductions (based on 60 percent business use) of $7,000. Val eventually sold the plane for $12,000. What is Val's deductible loss, or taxable gain, on the sale of the plane?

PROBLEM SET 16-2

¶ 16.03 CLOSED AND COMPLETED TRANSACTION REQUIREMENT; ¶ 16.04 INSURANCE OR OTHER COMPENSATION; ¶ 16.05 AMOUNT DEDUCTIBLE; ¶ 16.07 ANCILLARY MATTERS

(a)   Danny Developer purchased a city block on the edge of downtown Gotham. The purchase price of $1.2 million included $1 million for land and $200,000 for buildings. Danny rented the buildings to the then-current tenants for another three years, prior to demolishing them to construct a new office building at a cost of $10 million. At the time the buildings were demolished, their adjusted bases were $150,000. Danny incurred $50,000 of expenses to demolish them. What is his loss deduction for abandonment of the old buildings? What is his basis in the land? What is his basis in the new building?

(b)   (1)   What would be your answer to part (a) if, immediately after Danny had purchased the buildings, he had evicted the tenants and boarded up the buildings, and then, three years later, when the basis was still $200,000, the buildings had burned to the ground? In which year may Danny recognize any allowable loss?

        (2)   What would be the result if Danny received $80,000 of insurance proceeds on the buildings?

        (3)   What would be the result if the insurance company delayed payment, pending an investigation of possible arson, and the next year paid Danny $60,000 in full satisfaction of the insurance claim?

(c)   The Shortline Railroad Co. removed Engine No. 9 from service because it was no longer cost-effective to repair it. At the time of retirement, the adjusted basis of the engine was $5,000. Engine No. 9 was in such bad shape that it could have been sold only for scrap, for which it would have brought $2,000. Instead, Shortline Railroad parked it behind the maintenance shed, covered it with a tarpaulin, and occasionally cannibalized it for spare parts. When and in what amount may Shortline claim a loss deduction for Engine No. 9?

(d)   Why does IRC § 165(b) limit the amount of a loss to basis, even if the fair market value of a property at some point before it becomes worthless increases to an amount in excess of basis?

(e)   Television Broadcasting Corp. operates television station WWWK in Walla Walla, Kansaska. It recently abandoned its network affiliation with American Television Company (ATC) in favor of a network affiliation with National Television Systems (NTS). May Television Broadcasting Corp. deduct as a loss the $100,000 basis in its ATC franchise contract?

PROBLEM 16-3

¶ 16.06 STATUTORY LIMITATIONS ON LOSS DEDUCTIONS

(a)   (1)   Wendy Welloff sold 1,000 shares of stock in Leviathan Corp. to her adult son, Wendell, for $20,000 (which was their fair market value). Wendy had purchased the shares two years ago for $30,000. Thirteen months after he bought them, Wendell sold the shares through his stockbroker for $25,000. What are the tax consequences to Wendy and Wendell?

        (2)   How would your answer be different if Wendell had sold the shares for $35,000?

        (3)   How would your answer be different if Wendell had sold the shares for $15,000?

        (4)   How would your answers to parts (a)(2) and (a)(3) be different if Wendell had sold the shares eleven months after he purchased them?

        (5)   How would your answers be different in each of parts (a)(1) through (a)(4) if Wendy had sold the shares to her husband William?

(b)   Wendy Welloff sold 1,000 shares of Worldwide Business Equipment Corp. on the New York Stock Exchange for $40,000. Her basis in the shares was $50,000. That same day, she suggested to her adult son, Wellington, that he purchase for himself 500 shares of Worldwide Business Equipment Corp. stock. Wellington immediately purchased 500 shares in his own name for $20,200. Wellington sold the shares for

75

$30,000 eight months later. Does IRC § 267 have any application to these facts?

(c)   (1)   Sam Speculator purchased a tract of undeveloped land several years ago for $20,000. This year, when its value was $15,000, Sam sold the land to Acres Corp. for $15,000. Sam's wife owns 50 percent of the stock of Acres Corp., and his wife's sister owns 50 percent. Sam's wife's sister is otherwise unrelated to Sam. May Sam deduct his loss?

    (2)   What would be your answer if Sam's two brothers owned Acres Corp. in equal shares?

    (3)   What would be your answer if Acres Corp. were wholly owned by Sam's first cousin?

(d)   Betty Broker owned a parcel of real estate that she held for investment, in which she had a basis of $5,000. When Betty failed to pay $100 of real estate taxes, the city sold the land at public auction pursuant to state statute. At the auction, Betty's half-sister, Ruth Rich, purchased the land for $100. May Betty claim the $4,900 loss?

(e)   (1)   Irene Investor purchased 100 shares of Leviathan Corp. common stock for $20,000 on January 1. On November 30, she sold the shares for $15,000, and on December 31 she purchased another 100 shares of Leviathan Corp. common stock for $17,000. How much loss may Irene recognize? What is her basis in her Leviathan shares?

    (2)   What would be your answer if Irene had made the second purchase on December 30?

    (3)   Suppose Irene purchased 100 shares of Leviathan Corp. common stock for $20,000 on January 1, purchased an additional 100 shares on December 1 for $15,000, and sold 100 shares on December 31 for $17,000. How much gain or loss would she recognize on the sale, and what would be her basis in the remaining stock?

    (4)   Suppose Irene purchased 100 shares of Leviathan Corp. common stock for $20,000 on January 1, purchased an additional 100 shares on December 1 for $25,000, and sold 100 shares on December 31 for $24,000. How much gain or loss would she recognize on the sale?

(5)   What would be your answer to part (a)(2) if the purchase on December 30 had been by Irene's husband?

(6)   What would be your answer to part (a)(2) if, on December 30, Irene had purchased 100 shares of $20 par value nonconvertible preferred stock of Leviathan Corp.?

17

Bad Debts

PROBLEM SET 17-1

¶¶ 17.01–17.08 (THE ENTIRE CHAPTER)

(a) Last year, Lynn Lawyer, a cash method taxpayer, performed the legal work to establish Chimera Corp. and billed the corporation for $750, of which $50 represented the reimbursement for the cost of purchasing a corporate minute book and seal. This year, Chimera Corp. ceased doing business and became inactive, but was not dissolved, after having paid only $100 of the bill. How much may Lynn deduct as a bad debt?

(b) (1) Raet Apartments Corp. is an accrual method taxpayer in the apartment business. All rents are due on the first of the month in advance. As of the beginning of this year, there were past-due rents of $10,000 attributable to last year. Tenants who moved and left no forwarding address owe $6,000 of the arrears; tenants currently in the building owe $3,000; and each of two tenants who have moved to a neighboring state, for whom the management of Raet has forwarding addresses, owe $500. What portion of the past-due rents, if any, may Raet deduct as bad debts?

(2) What would be the tax consequences to Raet if, next year, an honest former tenant paid past-due rent that had been deducted as a bad debt this year?

(c) Last January, Clara Cash, who devotes all of her time to managing her investment portfolio, lent $10,000 to Ike Inventor to finance Ike's research projects. Ike signed a promissory note that was due in two years. It provided for 10 percent interest and that Clara could convert the debt into a 25 percent interest in any patents developed by Ike during the two-year period. Ike failed miserably. By this December, he was insolvent and had filed for bankruptcy. May Clara claim a bad-debt deduction? What is its character?

Accrual tax payes : yes, accrued
not paid
int'l added to
basis

79

cash   ''   4

NO.

(d) (1) Cathy Creditor lent $10,000 to her son Danny, who agreed to repay the loan at the rate of $1,000 of principal plus 10 percent interest on the outstanding balance each year. The debt was neither represented by a promissory note nor secured. After making one annual payment, Danny stopped making payments, and he now has no assets. May Cathy claim a bad-debt deduction for the $9,000 unpaid balance?

(2) What would be your answer if Danny had signed a promissory note and given Cathy a second mortgage on his house, but when Danny was forced into involuntary bankruptcy and the house was sold, the entire proceeds went to satisfy senior lienholders, and Cathy received only $100 when all claims were paid? What will be the character of any deduction that is allowed?

(e) (1) Last National Bank, an accrual method taxpayer, lent Harry Homeowner $40,000 to purchase a house from Sid Seller. Harry defaulted and is now hopelessly insolvent. On December 31, the bank sold the property at auction for $35,000, which was applied toward the $36,000 principal still due on the debt and the $3,000 of accrued but unpaid interest debt. What are the tax consequences to Last National Bank?

(2) What would be your answer if the bank was the only bidder at $38,000, and, on January 2, the bank sold the property to Randy Realtor for $39,000?

(f) (1) Jane Juggle runs an accounting firm as a sole proprietorship. She has two employees, her adult son Fred and Sam Stranger (who is not related to Jane). Sam desperately wants to buy a Porsche, but he cannot qualify for a loan. He tells Jane, and says he will look for a higher paying job unless Jane guarantees his loan. Jane agrees. Upon hearing of this, Fred decides he wants a Porsche too and presents Jane with the same ultimatum. Jane again agrees. Sam totals his car in an accident and stops making loan payments. Jane takes over the loan, making payments according to the original loan schedule. Is Jane entitled to a bad-debt deduction?

(2) What if it is Fred who has the accident and stops making payments?

18

Interest Paid or Accrued
on Indebtedness

PROBLEM SET 18-1

¶¶ 18.01–18.06 (THE ENTIRE CHAPTER)

(a)   Danny Debtor borrowed $400,000 from Usury Bank and Trust Co. last year and paid $40,000 interest on the loan. How much of the interest may Danny, a cash-method taxpayer, currently deduct under the following circumstances?

    (1)   Danny used the proceeds to build a vacation home, which was completed on January 1 of this year. (See also ¶¶ 22.02[1], 22.02[3].)

    (2)   Danny used the proceeds to construct a new factory, which was completed on January 1 of this year.

    (3)   Danny used the proceeds to buy undeveloped land to be held as an investment. His gross income for the year consisted of $100,000 of salary, $20,000 of dividends, and $15,000 of interest on certificates of deposit.

(b)   (1)   Mrs. Eggers owned a house that she rented to tenants. The house had a fair market value of $100,000. She borrowed $40,000, secured by a mortgage on the house, and used the $40,000 to purchase a BMW automobile for her personal (i.e., nonbusiness) use. There were no other mortgages on the house. May she deduct any of the interest on the $40,000 loan?

    (2)   Would your answer to part (b)(1) be different if the house in question were Mrs. Eggers' home? See also ¶ 22.02[2].

(c)   (1)   Mrs. Helvering paid $80,000 of her own money (no borrowed funds) to purchase a corporate bond several years ago. During 2003, the bond paid $8,000 taxable interest income. On January 1, 2003, Mrs. Helvering borrowed $100,000, which she immediately used to purchase a $100,000 interest in a passive activity. Her 2003 interest expense on the $100,000 debt was $9,000, and her income from the passive activity (not taking into account the $9,000 interest expense) was $3,000. Her salary income for the year was $60,000. She has no other relevant items of income or expense. How will her $9,000 of interest expense be treated for tax purposes? (See also ¶ 19.05.)

(2)   Instead of proceeding as described in part (c)(1), Mrs. Helvering did the following in 2003. On January 1, she sold the bond for $80,000. On January 2, she borrowed $20,000 from a bank. Later on the same day, she used that borrowed $20,000 and the $80,000 from the sale of the bond to buy a $100,000 interest in a passive activity. On January 3, she borrowed an additional $80,000 from the bank, all of which she used to buy a bond identical to the one she sold two days before. During 2003, the income from the passive activity was $3,000, and the income from the bond was $8,000 (in both cases, not taking into account any interest expense). The 2003 interest expense on the $20,000 loan was $1,800, and the 2003 interest expense on the $80,000 loan was $7,200. Her 2003 salary income was $60,000. She had no other relevant items of income or expense. How should her $9,000 of interest expense be treated for tax purposes?

(d)   Last year, the Slipshod Construction Corp. built a condominium complex, with the purpose of selling condominium units to the general public. Slipshod spent $1 million building the complex. Of that $1 million, $700,000 came from a construction loan, and $300,000 came from Slipshod's cash reserves. During the time that the complex was being built (which was all of last year), Slipshod paid $70,000 interest on the loan. The condominium complex was Slipshod's only active project last year. Slipshod did, however, own a parcel of land that it hoped to develop in the near future. There was a $400,000 mortgage on that land, and, last year, Slipshod paid $40,000 interest on the mortgage loan. How much, if any, of Slipshod's interest expense must be capitalized as part of the cost of the condominium complex?

19

Business Operating Losses and Tax Shelter Deductions

PROBLEM SET 19-1

¶ 19.02 NET OPERATING LOSS CARRYBACKS AND CARRYOVERS

(a)   Lenny and Lisa Loser, who are married and file joint returns, own and operate a Laundromat. Last year, the Laundromat generated $20,000 of gross income and $30,000 of business deductions. Lenny and Lisa were entitled to personal exemptions of $5,000 and a standard deduction of $6,500. What is their net operating loss (NOL) carryover from last year?

(b)   Lenny and Lisa carried the NOL computed in part (a) back to the previous year, for which their tax liability had originally been computed as follows:

1.	Gross income	$42,000
2.	Alimony payment	($ 2,000)
3.	Adjusted gross income (AGI)	$40,000
4.	Home mortgage interest	($ 6,000)
5.	Medical expenses ($5,000 actually spent, but deductible only to the extent it exceeds 7.5 percent of AGI)	($ 2,000)
6.	Personal exemptions	($ 5,000)
7.	Taxable income	$27,000
8.	Tax liability	$ 4,050

Assuming all their taxable income is taxed at the rate of 15 percent, recompute their tax liability for the previous year, in light of the NOL carryback.

(c)   Peaches Computer Corp. has had a checkered earnings history since its incorporation in 1996. Before taking NOL carrybacks and carryforwards into account, Peaches' taxable income had been as follows: 1996, ($1,000); 1997, $30,000; 1998, $20,000; 1999, $0; 2000, $10,000; 2001, ($50,000); 2002, $20,000; 2003, $20,000; 2004 ($10,000); 2005, $50,000. Recompute Peaches' taxable income for each of the years after taking into account NOL carrybacks and carryforwards.

PROBLEM SET 19-2

¶ 19.04 "AT RISK" LIMITATION ON LOSSES

(a)   (1)   Donna Dentist invested $10,000 to become a one-tenth partner in a partnership that was formed to buy a diesel railroad locomotive and lease it to Shortline Railroad. The partnership paid $1 million for the diesel locomotive by giving the seller $100,000 cash and a $900,000 promissory note payable only out of the net rents received or the proceeds from the sale of the locomotive. During the first year, accelerated cost recovery system (ACRS) deductions and interest expenses on the locomotive exceeded rents by $200,000. Do the at-risk rules limit the amount of her $20,000 share of the loss that Donna may deduct?

(2)   In the second year, rents received for the locomotive exceeded ACRS deductions and interest by $50,000; Donna's share of the profits was $5,000. What are the tax consequences to Donna?

(b)   (1)   What would be the result in parts (a)(1) and (a)(2) if the investing partners had been personally liable on the purchase-money promissory note?

(2)   What would be the result in part (b)(1) if, after two years, the recourse promissory note was sold by the original lender to one of the partners?

(c)   What would be the result in part (a)(1) if, instead of a diesel locomotive, the partnership had purchased an apartment building, and the $900,000 loan had been a nonrecourse loan from a bank, secured by the apartment building?

(d)   What would be the results in parts (a)(1) and (a)(2) if the rents for the first year exceeded the deductions by $20,000 and, in each of the second and third years, the deductions exceeded the rents by $20,000?

(e)   (1)   What would be the results in parts (a)(1) and (a)(2) if the taxpayer were Diversified Investment Corp., which is owned equally by eight unrelated shareholders?

        (2)   What would be the result in part (e)(1) if Diversified Investment Corp. had eleven equal, unrelated shareholders?

PROBLEM SET 19-3

¶ 19.05 PASSIVE ACTIVITY DEDUCTIONS AND LOSSES

(a)   (1)   Early in 2003, Sally Shelter, a wealthy attorney, purchased an office building for $1 million. The entire purchase price of the building came from "qualified nonrecourse financing" (IRC § 465(b)(6)) from a bank; Sally invested none of her own money. Sally did not devote any of her own time to managing the office building. During 2003, Sally received $110,000 of rental income from the building (net of all expenses except interest and depreciation). She paid $105,000 of interest on the loan. She also made a $10,000 principal payment on the note. The ACRS deduction on the building was $30,000 (although the actual decline in the value of the building was only $10,000). Sally had $500,000 of income from her law practice and $60,000 of dividends from stock investments. Assuming there is no other relevant information, what are the tax consequences in 2003 of Sally's investment in the office building?

        (2)   Suppose that on January 1, 2004, Sally sells the building. Since the value of the building exactly equals the $990,000 mortgage on the building, the only consideration she receives is the buyer's taking the building subject to the mortgage. What will be the tax consequences of the sale to Sally? (Assume that Sally is entitled to no ACRS deductions on the building in the year of sale.)

85

(3)   Now suppose that Sally did not sell the building in 2004, and that in 2004 she had $160,000 of rental income from the building (net of all expenses except interest and depreciation), $100,000 of interest expense on the loan, and a $30,000 ACRS deduction. Her income from her law practice and her dividend income are the same as in 2003. Assuming there is no other relevant information, what are the tax consequences in 2004 of Sally's investment in the office building?

(4)   What would be the tax consequences in part (a)(1) if Sally had another activity—ownership of a second office building—that produced income (net of all expenses, including interest and depreciation) of $20,000 in 2003?

(5)   What would be the tax consequences in part (a)(1) if Sally paid cash for the office building, and so incurred no interest expense?

(6)   Describe the difference in treatment of the ACRS deduction in part (a)(1) and in part (a)(5). Is this difference justified?

(b)   Pat Passive is involved in two related business undertakings, A and B. In each of the following circumstances, would Pat be better off if the two undertakings were treated as one activity, or as two?

(1)   Pat does not materially participate in either undertaking. There are substantial IRC § 469(b) passive loss carryforwards with respect to each undertaking. Pat sells his entire interest in A, but retains his interest in B.

(2)   Pat materially participates in A, but not in B. During the current year, A generates a loss of $50,000, and B generates a loss of $75,000. Pat has a salary of $150,000. There are no other relevant facts.

(3)   Pat materially participates in A, but not in B. During the current year, A produces income of $50,000, and B produces income of $75,000. Pat also has a $60,000 loss from passive activity C, which is clearly an activity separate from both A and B. There are no other relevant facts.

(c)   Lois Loss is a doctor, who earned a salary of $120,000 in 2003. She owns two apartment buildings. During 2003, Building A generated a loss of $40,000, and Building B produced income of $25,000. The two buildings constituted separate activities, and Lois actively participated in both activities. Lois also had $10,000 income in 2003 from a non-real estate passive activity. There are no other relevant facts. To what extent (if at all) may Lois deduct the loss from Building A?

21

Personal Exemptions and Itemized Deductions

PROBLEM SET 21-1

¶ 21.01 PERSONAL AND DEPENDENCY EXEMPTIONS; ¶ 21.02 QUALIFYING FACTORS FOR DEPENDENCY EXEMPTIONS; ¶ 21.04 THE STANDARD DEDUCTION

(a)   (1)   On December 29, John, who is 66 years old, married Priscilla, who is 60 years old and blind. If John had a gross income of $100,000 and files a separate return, how many personal exemptions may he claim, and how large an additional standard deduction may he claim, under the following circumstances?

         (i)   On the preceding January 2, Priscilla inherited $1,000 that she invested in a municipal bond that earned $80 of interest during the year.

         (ii)   On the preceding January 2, Priscilla invested in a bank certificate of deposit that earned $90 of interest during the year.

         (iii)   Priscilla had no income, but died on December 30.

   (2)   What should John and Priscilla do to maximize their available personal exemptions in part (a)(1)(ii)?

(b)   If Priscilla had been married to Roger, who died on January 2 of the same year in which Priscilla later married John, may both John and Priscilla, on their joint return, and Roger's executor, when filing Roger's final tax return, claim a personal exemption for Priscilla?

(c)   Howard and Marion file a joint return, although all of the income reported on the return is earned by Howard. May they claim a dependency exemption for their children under the following circumstances?

(1)   Richie is 20 years old and a full-time college student. He earned $4,000 last year that he used to pay college expenses. Howard and Marion contributed another $4,000 toward Richie's college expenses and provided him with free room and board at home during the summer.

(2)   The facts are the same as in part (c)(1), except that Richie earned $6,000 last year, which he used to buy a car and pay 50 percent of his college expenses.

(3)   The facts are the same as in part (c)(1), except that Richie earned only $2,000, which he used to buy a car, and he received a $4,100 scholarship from State University.

(4)   The facts are the same as in part (c)(1), except that Richie borrowed $4,100 from State University to pay part of his college expenses.

(5)   Joanie is 19 years old and graduated from high school in June. From June to December, she traveled through Europe on a trip paid for by Howard. On December 31, she married Charlie, and they filed a joint return.

(d)   John B. Tipton, a generous man, totally supports numerous members of his extended family. With respect to which of the following may he claim a dependency exemption?

(1)   His uncle, who has no income and lives in an apartment for which John pays the rent.

(2)   His cousin and her son, who have no income and live in an apartment for which John pays the rent.

(3)   Same as part (d)(2), except that they live in John's house.

(4)   Same as part (d)(3), except that John's cousin earned $3,000 selling pottery at craft shows.

(e)   What is the total amount of personal and dependency exemptions in each of the following situations? (Ignore the inflation adjustments to the statutory amount for personal and dependency exemptions).

(1)   Georges lives alone and has a management position with the New York Yankees. His adjusted gross income (AGI) is $140,000.

(2)   Kristen and Marc are newlyweds, so this year they are going to file a joint return. Kristen is an attorney and Marc is the CEO of a small corporation. Their combined AGI is $250,000.

(3)   Nancy is divorced with two children she is entitled to claim as dependents; her AGI is $150,000.

(f)   (1)   What is the rationale for dependency exemptions?

        (2)   Consider two married couples. Each couple has $300,000 AGI. Couple *A* has eight dependent children; Couple *B* has none. What will be the difference in the taxable incomes of the two couples (assuming no other relevant information)?

        (3)   What does your answer to part (f)(1) suggest about the appropriateness of the result in part (f)(2)?

        (4)   Assuming the explicit marginal tax rate on taxable income above $200,000 is 40 percent, what would be the effective marginal rate faced by Couple *A* if they had $250,000 AGI?

PROBLEM SET 21-2

¶ 21.02 QUALIFYING FACTORS FOR DEPENDENCY EXEMPTIONS

(a)   Grandma is 87 years old and living in a nursing home. She has no income and is entirely supported by her Daughter, Grandson, and Granddaughter. Daughter and Grandson each provide 45 percent of Grandma's support; Granddaughter provides 10 percent of Grandma's support. Who may claim a dependency exemption for Grandma?

(b)   (1)   Mom and Dad were divorced in 2001. Daughter spends eight months with Mom and four months with Dad each year; Son lives with Dad for eight months and Mom for four months each year. Dad provides $3,000 to support Daughter and $3,000 to support Son each year; Mom provides $2,000 to support Son and $2,000 to support Daughter each year. Grandpa provides $1,000 for each child each year. Who is entitled to a dependency exemption for Son and for Daughter?

        (2)   May Mom and Dad allocate the dependency exemption by agreement?

        (3)   If Daughter is 18 years old, goes to college, and spends only two months of the year with Mom and one month with Dad, who will be entitled to the dependency exemption if:

91

     (i)   Mom provides over 50 percent of Daughter's support?

     (ii)   Dad provides over 50 percent of Daughter's support?

     (iii)   Grandpa provides 60 percent of Daughter's support for the year by paying most of her educational expenses, and Mom and Dad each contribute 20 percent of Daughter's support for the year?

PROBLEM SET 21-3

¶ 21.03 ADJUSTED GROSS INCOME AND ITEMIZED DEDUCTIONS; ¶ 21.04 THE STANDARD DEDUCTION

(a)   Harvey and Harriet Healthy are married, have no children, and had AGI of $40,000 last year. The Healthys had no itemized tax deductions last year. The Healthys' neighbors, Sam and Samantha Sickley, are also married, without children, and had AGI of $40,000 last year. The Sickleys incurred an unexpected uninsured medical expense of $7,500; other than that, they had no itemized deductions. What are the taxable incomes of the Healthys and Sickleys? Do the Healthys and Sickleys have identical disposable incomes before paying federal income taxes?

(b)   John's AGI is $150,000, and his official marginal tax rate (under IRC § 1) is 30 percent (a hypothetically assumed rate). His total itemized deductions, before reduction under IRC § 68, are $40,000. What will be the tax consequences to John under IRC § 68 if he earns another $10,000, increasing his AGI to $160,000? What will be the tax consequences to John under IRC § 68 if he does not earn another $10,000, but he gives another $10,000 to his favorite charity (increasing his pre-IRC § 68 itemized deductions to $50,000)?

(c)   Alice and Marie are tax professors at different law schools. Each is paid a salary of $100,000, and each considers a subscription to Tax Notes to be absolutely essential to doing her job. Alice's employer pays for her subscription (which costs $500 per year), but Marie pays for her subscription out of her own pocket. What are the tax consequences of their subscriptions? (In Marie's case, assume she itemizes deductions, and that none of her other deductions are miscellaneous itemized deductions.)

22

Personal Interest

¶ 22.01 NONDEDUCTIBLE PERSONAL INTEREST; ¶ 22.02 DEDUCTION FOR "QUALIFIED RESIDENCE INTEREST," ¶ 22.03 SPECIAL PROBLEMS

(a)   (1)   When Peter Piper purchased a new home for $70,000, he financed $50,000 of the purchase price with a mortgage loan from the Last National Bank. In addition to the interest component of each mortgage payment, Peter paid the bank the following amounts, for the stated purposes, at or before the closing:

Loan application fee	$ 100
Credit report fee (for Credit Reporting Agency)	$ 100
Lawyer fee (for title opinion and drafting mortgage and note)	$ 300
Loan closing fee (2 percent of principal)	$1,000

$7000's deductible

Which, if any, of these fees may Peter deduct as interest? When may he deduct it?

      (2)   What would your answer be if, instead of Peter paying the bank $1,500 and the bank disbursing $50,000 to the seller in addition to Peter's $20,000 payment, the bank had disbursed $48,500 to the seller and Peter had paid the seller $21,500, but nevertheless executed a promissory note for $50,000?

      (3)   What would be your answer to part (a)(1) if Peter were an accrual method taxpayer and had purchased a building in which to operate his used comic book store?

      (4)   What would be your answer to part (a)(3) if Peter were a cash method taxpayer?

(b)   (1)   Donna Debt owns a house, which she uses as her principal residence, with a basis of $60,000 and a value of $100,000.

There is a $20,000 mortgage on the home, which Donna incurred in buying the house. On January 1 of the current year, Donna borrows $70,000, secured by a second mortgage on the house, and uses the borrowed money to buy $70,000 of common stock in Growth Corp. During the year, Donna pays $2,000 interest on the first mortgage loan and $7,000 interest on the second mortgage loan. She also receives $3,000 of dividends on the Growth Corp. stock. She has no other investments and owes no other debts. To what extent, if at all, may she deduct the $7,000 interest paid on the second mortgage? *$7000 is allowed deduct or*

(2) *matters whether* The facts are the same as in part (b)(1), except that Donna uses the $70,000 to buy $70,000 of municipal bonds. During the year, the bonds pay $5,000 of tax-exempt interest. To what extent, if at all, may Donna deduct the $7,000 interest paid on the second mortgage?

all $70000 is invested in tax-exempt securities

$0 is deduct b/c

(c) *Here all 100% is invested in tax exempt sec the whole $7000 is not deductible* Daddy Warbucks decided to stop renting an apartment and to purchase his own home. Because he was about to adopt a daughter (and her dog), he decided to build a big $3 million house on the banks of the Hudson. He paid a down payment of $1.5 million, and borrowed the rest (the loan was secured by the house). During year 1, Daddy Warbucks paid $150,000 in interest on the debt. How much, if any, of his interest expense is deductible?

(d)   (1)   Ranger Rick loves camping; ever since he was a little boy, he has camped in every season of the year. Rick's wife Zelda, however, hates sleeping on the ground in tents. Zelda and Rick decided to compromise and buy some modern camping equipment. They shopped around and came up with three different options: (1) a pop-up camper that sleeps six, has a kitchen, a stove, and a sink, and also has electric and water hookups; (2) a motor home that has everything that the pop-up has, plus a toilet; and (3) a boat that sleeps four and has a kitchen area with a stove, a toilet, a shower bag, and a generator for electricity.

       Rick and Zelda have to take out a loan for whichever option they choose, and they already have a purchase-money mortgage on their home of $150,000, and a home equity loan for $100,000 (which went towards a Mercedes-Benz and a month-long vacation in Bali). Which, if any, of the three options would qualify as a secondary residence and be eligible for acquisition indebtedness treatment under IRC § 163(h)(4)(a)(i)(II)?

(2) Suppose Rick and Zelda already have a motor home with a $50,000 debt, which they have claimed as a second residence for the past five years. They now decide to get a boat too, which will require a loan of $175,000. How much of the two loans will qualify as acquisition indebtedness and generate deductible interest under IRC § 163(h)(4)(a)(i)(II)?

(e) (1) Barbara has a $400,000 mortgage (all of which constitutes acquisition indebtedness) on her principal residence. She is considering buying a second home, with the purchase financed in part by a $250,000 loan (which would be secured by a mortgage on the second home). If she does buy the second home, her plan is to let her adult child live in the house rent-free for the next several years. If Barbara goes through with this plan, will she be able to deduct her interest payments on the mortgage on the second residence?

(2) Suppose Barbara has a different plan for the second home. She intends to rent it out (at the market rate) for forty-four weeks of the year, and to live in it herself for eight weeks every summer. In that case would she be entitled to deduct her interest payments on the mortgage on the second residence?

23

Taxes

¶¶ 23.01–23.02 (THE ENTIRE CHAPTER)

(a) (1) Mr. and Mrs. Moneybags gave their second home to their son Chip. Last year, Chip was a bit strapped for cash, so his parents paid the $2,000 real property tax assessed against the home from their own funds. Who may deduct the $2,000?

(2) Chip paid the city $500 of sewer use charges, which are assessed on the basis of water consumption. May Chip deduct the sewer use charges?

(3) Chip paid the city a special tax assessment of $2,000 for the cost of installing new sidewalks and lights and repaving the streets. May Chip deduct the $2,000?

(b) Sam Shopkeeper paid $1,000 of real estate taxes on his store and $700 of real estate taxes on his home last year. Sam, who is single, had no other personal deductions. How much of the $1,700 of taxes may Sam deduct?

(c) Bill Bassbuster was required to pay $123 to register his boat with the state of Missabama. Of that amount, the fee for the license sticker was $20 (based on the length of the boat), and the other $103 was a tax on one percent of the value of the boat. Bill also paid a fee of $210 to license his pickup truck. Of that amount, $10 was for the license plate and $200 was a 2 percent tax on the value of the truck. To what extent are these payments deductible?

(d) (1) Sarah Seller sold her home to Betty Buyer for $50,000. When the closing was held on April 1, Betty paid Sarah $50,753, because, on February 1, Sarah had paid the city real estate taxes of $1,000 for the year ending on the following December 31. Under state law, the real estate taxes are the personal liability of the owner of the house on January 1. What portion of the real estate taxes assessed against the house is deductible by Sarah and what portion is deductible by Betty?

(2)   What would your answer be if Betty had paid Sarah $50,000 at the closing and Betty had paid the $1,000 tax bill on August 1?

(e)   (1)   Frank Fisher lives in Vancouver, Washington. Washington State has a sales tax, but no income tax. Frank paid $5,000 of state sales tax last year. Leo Logger lives across the river in Portland, Oregon. Oregon has an income tax, but no sales tax. Leo paid $5,000 in state income tax last year. What are the amounts of Frank's and Leo's deductions under IRC § 164?

(2)   Are the results in part (e)(1) fair?

24

Casualty Losses

PROBLEM SET 24-1

¶¶ 24.01–24.05 (THE ENTIRE CHAPTER)

(a)   (1)   Last year, Phil Painter purchased a pickup truck to use exclusively in his business. Early this year, a tree Phil was cutting down fell on his truck while it was parked in his driveway. Before the accident, the adjusted basis of the truck was $10,000, and its fair market value was $11,000. After the accident, the value of the truck was $2,000. Phil's insurance, however, paid only $5,000 of his $9,000 damage claim. What is the amount of Phil's casualty loss deduction? What is the basis of the truck?

   (2)   What would be Phil's casualty loss deduction if the adjusted basis of the truck was $10,000, the fair market value of the truck before the accident was $9,000, the fair market value of the truck after the accident was zero, Phil received no insurance proceeds, and the truck was scrapped?

   (3)   What would be Phil's casualty loss deduction in part (a)(2) if the vehicle involved were Phil's automobile (instead of a pickup truck), used solely for personal purposes, and Phil's adjusted gross income (AGI) for the year were $30,000?

   (4)   What would be Phil's casualty loss deduction if the tree that Phil cut down fell on Neil Neighbor's car, which was parked on the street, and Phil (whose insurance paid only $5,000 of the $9,000 damage claim) paid Neil an additional $4,000 in full settlement of the claim?

(b)   (1)   Ursula Unfortunate suffered a terrible year last year. In March, her apartment was burglarized, and her gold jewelry valued at $3,000 was stolen. The jewelry, which was never recovered, was quite old and had a basis of only $1,000. Ursula's insurance coverage was limited to $2,000. In July, her automobile was stolen and never recovered. The automobile

99

had a basis of $3,000, a fair market value of $1,000, and was not insured for theft loss. Ursula's AGI for the year was $8,000. What is the amount of her casualty loss deduction?

    (2)   Would your answer be different if the fair market value of the car were $2,100?

(c)   Lee Littoral owns an improved parcel of oceanfront land and an adjacent parcel of improved land separated from the ocean only by the oceanfront parcel. Lee uses the oceanfront parcel as a vacation home. The other parcel Lee holds for rent. A recent winter storm eroded the dunes on the oceanfront parcel, and its fair market value diminished from $120,000 to $100,000. The adjacent parcel only diminished in value from $100,000 to $95,000, since the risk of future damage was not as great. Each property had a basis of $80,000. What is Lee's casualty loss deduction for the year?

(d)   Luther Richey met a man who convinced him that he had invented a process to reproduce U.S. currency by bleaching out a $1 bill and transferring the ink from a $100 bill to the $1 bill. The man promised Richey $5,000 (to be obtained by exchanging the counterfeit bills for real bills at a bank) if Richey would provide 15,000 $1 bills to be bleached for reprinting as $100 bills. Convinced that the process worked, and always ready to make some easy money, Richey withdrew $15,000 from his bank account and met the man in a hotel room with the cash. Richey and the man began to bleach out a $100 packet of bills, but before the process had substantially begun, the man left the room with the remaining $14,900 on the pretext of running an errand. Richey claimed a theft loss when filing his tax return for the year. Should it be allowed?

(e)   (1)   Betty Bookkeeper handled all of the bookkeeping, payroll, billings, and bank deposits for Sam Shopkeeper. Last year, Betty Bookkeeper embezzled $20,000. Her malefaction was discovered this year, and Betty promised Sam that she would pay it back if he would not turn her in to the police. Sam, having a heart of gold, agreed, and, on July 31, Betty began paying the $20,000 back at the rate of $40 per week out of her wages as a custodian. (Sam now keeps the books.) When and in what amount may Sam claim a theft loss?

(2) Suppose the same basic facts as in part (e)(1), but that by the time Sam discovered the theft Betty had disappeared, and there is no realistic possibility of recovering anything from Betty. Betty had been bonded, however, for $20,000. Sam could have been compensated for his entire loss by filing a report with the police and a claim with the insurance company, but he elected not to because his heart of gold could not bear putting the police on Betty's trail. May Sam deduct the $20,000 loss?

(f) Paul Pyro and his wife, Phyllis, owned a home in Richmond. Paul's employer transferred him to Atlanta, but Phyllis refused to move. After a month in Atlanta, Paul returned to Richmond, to attempt to persuade Phyllis to move. Much to his surprise, Paul discovered that Phyllis was living with another man. Paul waited until Phyllis and the man had left the house. He then entered the house and set fire to some of Phyllis' clothes, to express his displeasure. The fire spread, and the house burned down. Paul claimed that although he intended to burn the clothes, he did not intend to burn down the house. Is Paul entitled to a casualty loss deduction?

(g) You recently inherited a painting worth $100,000. Because it has great sentimental value to you, you want to hang it in your living room (rather than keep it in a bank vault). In deciding whether or not to insure it, are you at all influenced by the rules for casualty loss deductions? Does it matter whether (1) your AGI is $300,000 and your marginal tax rate is 40 percent or (2) your AGI is $20,000 and your marginal tax rate is 15 percent?

25

Charitable Contributions

PROBLEM SET 25-1

¶¶ 25.01–25.05 (THE ENTIRE CHAPTER)

(a)   (1)   Jack Sweatsox, a fan of the State University football team, was informed, when he attempted to buy season tickets, that the only tickets available to the general public (at a price of $100 per season ticket) were in the last row of the upper deck of the stadium. However, two season tickets were available in the first row of the upper deck for any member of the Booster Club, and two season tickets were available in the lower level for members of the Touchdown Club. One could become an annual member of the Booster Club by giving $600 to the University Athletic Scholarship Fund, and one could become a member of the Touchdown Club by giving $1,000 to the fund. Jack gave $1,000 to the fund, but, by his own choice, purchased two upper-deck season tickets in the Booster Club priority seating area at a price of $100 for each season ticketbook. How much of the $1,200 that Jack gave to State University is deductible as a charitable contribution?

           (2)   If Jack is a sporting goods salesman, how might he treat any portion of his payment that is not a charitable contribution if he uses the season tickets for business entertainment?

(b)   (1)   Lucy Lawyer prepared the corporate charter and bylaws of the Smalltown Girls' Club. The work took her eight hours. She normally charges $75 an hour, but she billed the Girls' Club nothing. May Lucy deduct the value of the services for which she did not charge?

           (2)   Rhoda Realtor donated to the Girls' Club a one-acre parcel of unimproved land on which to build its meeting hall. Rhoda purchased the land two years ago for $5,000; its current fair market value is $10,000. What is the amount of Rhoda's charitable contribution?

(3)   Carl Carpenter built the Girls' Club meeting hall. Carl spent $20,000 for materials that would have cost $25,000 without his contractor's discount. The completed Girls' Club building had a fair market value of $30,000, but Carl charged the Girls' Club only $20,000. To insulate the Girls' Club from potential liability during construction, the Girls' Club had deeded the land to Carl before construction began, and Carl agreed to retransfer the land when construction was completed. What is the amount of Carl's charitable contribution?

(4)   Irene Investor donated 100 shares of stock of Specific Motors to the Girls' Club, which shortly thereafter sold the stock for $2,500 to pay operating expenses. Irene's basis in the stock when she purchased it two years ago was $1,000, and its fair market value on the day Irene contributed it was $2,000. What is the amount of Irene's charitable contribution? Would your answer be different if Irene had purchased the stock four months ago?

(5)   Carla Collector donated several pieces of antique furniture that she had owned for several years, which had a basis of $1,000 and which an antique dealer had recently offered to purchase for $4,000. The Girls' Club held a raffle to raise operating funds with the antiques as prizes; the raffle collected $8,000. What is the amount of Carla's charitable contribution?

(6)   Cathy Camp owns and operates a children's summer camp. Cathy allowed the Girls' Club the exclusive use of the facilities for one week in July. As a result, she lost revenues of $1,000. What is the amount of Cathy's charitable contribution?

(c)   Florence donated blood to the Red Cross once last year. The fair market value of her pint of blood (measured by what a local plasma center would have paid) was $50. What is her IRC § 170 deduction on account of her blood donation?

(d)   Lorna Lott owned undeveloped land that she purchased several years ago as an investment. She sold the land for $150,000 to Charitable Hospital, which planned to build a new wing on the land. Her basis in the land was $80,000, and the fair market value of the land was $200,000. What are the tax consequences of the sale to Lorna?

(e)   Last year, Barbara Benefactor's contribution base for charitable deductions was $100,000. Barbara's favorite charitable organizations are Ivy University and the Benefactor family's Private Charitable Foundation, which is an IRC § 170(c)(2) organization, but not an IRC § 170(b)(1)(A) organization. What would be the amount of Barbara's charitable contribution deduction for last year in each of the following circumstances?

   (1)   She gave $60,000 in cash to Ivy University.
   (2)   She gave $40,000 in cash to Ivy University and $20,000 in cash to the Private Foundation.
   (3)   She gave $10,000 in cash to Ivy University and $50,000 in cash to the Private Foundation.
   (4)   She gave shares of corporate stock that she had held for more than a year, with a basis of $48,000 and a fair market value of $50,000, to Ivy University.
   (5)   She gave Xerox stock, with a basis of $5,000 and a fair market value of $20,000, to Ivy University, and IBM stock, with a basis of $2,000 and a value of $15,000, to the Private Foundation. She had held both the Xerox and the IBM stock for many years.
   (6)   What is Barbara's carryforward of excess charitable contributions in each of parts (e)(1) through (e)(5)?

(f)   (1)   Fred Farmer deeded his farm to State University for eventual use by its College of Agriculture, reserving a life estate for himself. The fair market value of the remainder interest is $30,000. May Fred claim a charitable contribution deduction?
   (2)   Sam Shopkeeper deeded the parking lot next to his store to State University, reserving a life estate for himself. The fair market value of the remainder interest is $30,000. May Sam claim a charitable contribution deduction?

(g)   The Established Church of Christ has a long-standing policy, under which parishioners receive the right to occupy particular seats during Sunday services, in exchange for the payment of pew rents. Are the pew rents deductible under IRC § 170?

(h)   Ralph and Rita send their 10-year-old child to a religious school, which charges $15,000 annual tuition (which is approximately the same price

105

charged by secular private schools in the area). The school devotes 60 percent of instructional time to secular education, and the other 40 percent to religious instruction. May Ralph and Rita deduct $6,000 (40 percent of $15,000) as a charitable contribution, on the theory that (1) $6,000 of the tuition is allocable to the intangible religious benefits of religious instruction and (2) an intangible religious benefit does not count as a quid pro quo for purposes of IRC § 170?

(i)   The Metropolitan Museum of Natural History (MMNH) sells annual family memberships for $200. A family membership entitles anyone in the family to an unlimited number of free admissions during the year. MMNH informs members that the entire $200 cost of membership is deductible under IRC § 170 (for taxpayers who itemize their deductions). How can MMNH possibly justify this statement, given the rule that the amount of any charitable contribution deduction must be reduced by any value received by the taxpayer in return for the contribution?

(j)   Libby Dale pledged to contribute $3,000 in 2003 to the Red Cross (an IRC § 501(c)(3) organization) through payroll deductions. The only documentation Libby has of her contributions is a Form W-2 from her employer indicating that $3,000 was withheld from her 2003 pay and paid over to the Red Cross. Assuming Libby itemizes deductions, is she entitled to deduct the $3,000? Does it matter whether (1) Libby was paid monthly, and 1/12 of the $3,000 was withheld each month or (2) Libby was paid bi-weekly, and 1/26 of the $3,000 was withheld each pay period?

26

Medical and Dental Expenses

¶ 26.01 DEDUCTIBLE MEDICAL AND DENTAL EXPENSES; ¶ 26.02 ANCILLARY PROBLEMS

(a)   (1)   Jane and John Doe's 6-year-old daughter Mary suffers from severe rheumatoid arthritis. To reduce the inflammation of her joints and to ease her pain, her physician recommended that she swim every day for one hour and also spend about half an hour in a whirlpool bath. John and Jane decided the most practical approach was for Mary to join a swim club. On July 1, they accordingly paid, on Mary's behalf, $125 in initiation fees and $200 in annual dues to a swim club with an indoor pool. Because the club did not allow a child to join without an adult, John also joined the club, at the same expense. The club was about ten miles from the Does' house, and they made a round trip by car every day. Although Mary swam every day, John swam only once or twice a month. John was, however, always present when Mary swam. In addition, the Does purchased a portable indoor whirlpool bath. The least expensive model cost $2,000; the most expensive model cost $4,000. The Does bought one at the lower end of the price spectrum for $2,500. They did not want to buy the cheapest model because they also wanted one large enough for John to use for chronic lower back pain that flared up whenever he played golf. John and Jane also paid $400 of medical insurance premiums, $500 of physician bills for routine care, $1,000 to an orthodontist for braces for their 13-year-old daughter's teeth, $100 for prescription drugs, and $25 for over-the-counter medicines. They received a $300 reimbursement from their medical insurance policy. The Does' adjusted gross income last year was $30,000. What is the amount of their medical expense deduction?

(2)   By the end of last year, the Does decided that it was inconvenient to constantly drive their daughter to and from the pool. Since John's income had increased, they decided to build an addition to their house for an indoor pool. The cost of the basic pool was $8,000, with an additional cost of $2,000 for the diving board and ceramic tile options. The cost of the addition to the house was $20,000; the addition had room for the pool, a walkway around the pool, and a sitting area on one side. An addition could have been constructed for $12,000, but the Does opted to build a greenhouse over the pool to take advantage of the southern exposure and to provide a sitting area. The Does' electric bill increased by $200 last year as a result of operating the pool filter. Before the pool and addition were added, the fair market value of the Does' house was $80,000; after the addition was added its value was $100,000. The Does' adjusted gross income this year is $40,000. What is the amount of their medical expense deduction, assuming that they incurred no other medical expenses?

(b)   Grandma Aged, who was 85 years old, moved out of her apartment and into a nursing home where she could receive constant care. She could no longer get out of bed, because of a broken hip that had not properly healed. In exchange for care for the rest of her life at the nursing home, Grandma paid the home $50,000. This sum covered room, board, routine physician's care, medicine, and nursing services, as needed. Of this amount, $20,000 was nonrefundable, but if Grandma decided to leave the nursing home, she would be refunded the balance, less $6,000 for each year she had lived in the home. To what extent may Grandma deduct the $50,000 payment? May she deduct all or part of the amount that may not be deducted this year in a future year?

(c)   Suzie Snow, a 17-year-old high school student from Beverley Beach, California, entered the Kandi Drug Rehabilitation Clinic in an attempt to break her cocaine habit. While at the clinic, she was treated by physicians and psychiatrists, as well as staff sociologists and psychologists. Much of her time was spent in group sessions with other drug users. The cost of her treatment, which was paid by her father, was $4,000. When the drug user was a teenager, the Kandi Drug Rehabilitation Clinic's program involved sessions every other day with the child and her parents. Only Suzie's mother, Samantha, attended, however, because Samantha (who was divorced from Suzie's father) had custody of Suzie for most of the year. The Kandi Drug Rehabilitation Clinic was 500 miles from Samantha's home. Therefore, she took a room in the nearest Hyatt Regency for one month. Her room was $100 a day, and she spent $50 per day on meals for the thirty days she was near the Drug Rehabilitation Clinic, as well as $500 for one round-trip airline ticket between Beverley Beach and the Drug Rehabilitation Clinic. Suzie's father paid for Suzie's airline ticket. To what extent may Suzie's father and Samantha each take these expenses into account in computing their medical expense deductions?

(d) Dan Dentin, who is 40 years old, has long been self-conscious about his crooked teeth. Having come into some money lately, he decides to ask an orthodontist about braces. The orthodontist tells Dan braces will take two years and cost $15,000. Consider whether the cost of the braces would qualify for a medical expense deduction (subject to the 7.5 percent of AGI floor) in each of these variations:

(1) The orthodontist says the only benefit of straighter teeth for Dan is improved appearance.

(2) The orthodontist says the only benefit of straighter teeth for Dan is improved appearance, but Dan was referred to the orthodontist by Dan's psychiatrist, who believes Dan's self-consciousness about his teeth is causing him serious emotional problems.

(3) The orthodontist says the main benefit of braces for Dan will be cosmetic, but straighter teeth will also help prevent tooth decay and gum disease.

(4) If a deduction is available, should Dan consider paying the entire amount in the first year?

(e) Patrick and Michael O'Malley are twin brothers who both have leukemia. They work for different companies; Pat has AGI of $45,000, and the company pays his insurance premium of $2,000/year; Mike has AGI of $47,000 and pays his own insurance premium of $2,000/year. Because of their disease, Patrick and Michael each spent $8,500 on medical expenses this year; of that amount they each received $7,000 reimbursement from their respective insurance companies. How much, if any, of their medical expenses are deductible?

109

27

Personal Credits

PROBLEM SET 27-1

¶ 27.01 IN GENERAL; ¶ 27.02 EARNED INCOME CREDIT; ¶ 27.03 CHILD TAX CREDIT; ¶ 27.04 CARE OF EMPLOYED TAXPAYER'S SPOUSE, DEPENDENTS, AND HOUSEHOLD; ¶ 27.07 EDUCATION CREDITS

(a)   You serve on the staff of Representative Fisk, a member of the House Ways and Means Committee. He has asked you to analyze the merits of a bill to repeal IRC § 21, which grants a credit for certain dependent care expenses, and in its place to enact new IRC § 162(a)(4), which would specifically describe such expenses as trade or business expenses. He is particularly interested in knowing whether the proposed legislation is closer to or further from the theoretically correct treatment of such expenses than current law.

(b)   John and Mary Jobs both worked full-time last year. John earned $40,000, and Mary earned $50,000. Their adjusted gross income (AGI) was $90,000. They had two children, ages 3 and 5. They paid a nanny $10,000 to be with the children in their home while John and Mary were both at work. In addition to taking care of the children, the nanny also did a significant amount of house cleaning. What is the amount of the child care credit that John and Mary are entitled to claim for last year?

(c)   Lissa is an unmarried law student with no dependents. Her only income for this year is $5,000 from her summer job with a law firm. Is Lissa entitled to any earned income tax credit? Do you need more information to decide?

(d)   (1)   Lori is a single mother with two children, ages 4 and 6. She has a thirty-hours-a-week job at Wal-Mart, that pays $11,610 per year. She has been offered a full-time job that pays $15,610 a year. If she takes the job, what will be the effect on her earned income tax credit?

(2)   Lori decides to keep her $11,610 job. If she has a third child, what will be the effect on the amount of her earned income tax credit?

(e)   You are an IRS agent auditing the tips reported by wait persons employed by the Metropolitan Grill. You notice that one waitress, who had only $4,000 of wages, reported $4,000 of tips. No one else reported tips equal to more than half of wages. Have you found the world's most honest waitress, or do you suspect something else is going on?

(f)   Ward and June have two children, both of whom meet the IRC § 24(c) definition of a "qualifying child." If the "per child amount" (IRC § 24(a)(2)) for the current year is $600, and their AGI is $115,000, what is the total amount of Ward's and June's child tax credit?

(g)   Ruth is a sophomore attending State University. Her tuition expense for the current calendar year is $6,000, of which she is paying half and her parents are paying half. Her parents are entitled to claim Ruth as a dependent on their income tax return. Because of their high AGI (well over $200,000) and the effect of IRC § 151(d)(3), claiming Ruth as a dependent would reduce their income tax liability by only about $100. Ruth's AGI (from summer and part-time employment) is in the very low five-figure range, and her tax liability (pre-credit) is $1,000. What should Ruth and her parents do to take maximum advantage of the Hope Scholarship credit?

(h)   (1)   Ted and Tina are the parents of triplets, all of whom qualify as their tax dependents, and all of whom are sophomores at State University. This calendar year Ted and Tina will pay $6,000 of qualified tuition and related expenses with respect to each child. Ted's and Tina's AGI is below the phaseout threshold of IRC § 25A(d). What is the amount of their Hope Scholarship credit for this year?

        (2)   Suppose that the situation next year (2004) is exactly the same as this year, except all three children are in the junior year of college. Will Ted and Tina be able to claim the Hope Scholarship credit? Will they be able to claim the Lifetime Learning credit? If so, what will be the amount of the credit?

(i)   Mark is a college freshman in the first part of calendar year 2004, and a sophomore during the second half of the year. His qualified tuition and related expenses, all of which are paid by his parents, add up to $10,000. His parents are not subject to the AGI phaseout of IRC § 25A(d). Should his parents claim the Hope Scholarship credit, the Lifetime Learning credit, or both? (His parents did not make any other qualified tuition payments during the year.)

28

Realization of Gains and Losses—Taxable Events

PROBLEM SET 28-1

¶¶ 28.01–28.10 (THE ENTIRE CHAPTER)

(a)   (1)   Tiny Corporation has only two shares of stock outstanding. Both shares are owned by Mrs. Macomber, who has a $500 per share basis. (Mrs. Macomber created the corporation several years ago by transferring $1,000 to the corporation in exchange for the two shares.) The corporation has retained $500 of earnings, so each share is now worth $750. To celebrate, Mrs. Macomber causes Tiny to declare a stock dividend of one-half share for each existing share—in other words, Tiny issues one new share to Mrs. Macomber. Has Mrs. Macomber realized a gain?

        (2)   Does your answer to part (1) depend on the fact that Mrs. Macomber is no better off after the stock dividend than before (because 2 shares × $750 = 3 shares × $500)?

(b)   Nora Niece cared for her aged aunt, Thelma Testator, for twenty years after Thelma promised to leave her magnificent mansion, Lucreacre, to Nora upon her death. Nora and Thelma entered into a written contract memorializing the terms of the oral agreement. When she was 87 years old, Thelma suffered a stroke and entered a nursing home. It soon became apparent to her that she would never leave the nursing home during her life, so she deeded Lucreacre to Nora. It then had a fair market value of $1 million and a basis of $100,000. Must Thelma recognize any gain?

(c)   Samantha Settlor established two trusts, one for the benefit of each of her twin daughters, Buffy and Muffy. Samantha gave $100,000 to Buffy's trust, under which the trustee was to distribute to Buffy in cash or property half of the value of the trust assets when she became 21 years old, and the balance when she became 30. Samantha gave 1,000 shares of stock of Leviathan Oil Corp., which were worth $100,000 and had a basis of $50,000, to Muffy's trust. The trustee was to distribute half of the stock to Muffy when she became 21 years old, and the balance when she became 30. The trustee of Buffy's trust purchased 500 shares of stock in Leviathan Oil Corp. with half of the $100,000 cash corpus. When the twins became 21 years old, each trustee distributed to the respective beneficiary 500 shares of Leviathan Oil Corp. stock, which then had a fair market value of $100,000. How much gain must be recognized by each trustee?

(d)   Tom Trader owned fifty shares of stock in Black Corp., which had a basis of $1,000 and a fair market value of $50,000. Sam Swap owned 100 shares of stock in Blue Corp., which had a basis of $10,000 and a fair market value of $50,000. Tom gave his Black Corp. stock to Sam in exchange for Sam's Blue Corp. stock. How much gain must Tom and Sam each recognize?

(e)   (1)   Last January, Danny Debtor borrowed $75,000 from the Last National Bank, giving as security a mortgage on a small downtown commercial building owned by him, in which he had a basis of $50,000. It was a nonrecourse mortgage loan, and Danny used the proceeds to make an unrelated investment. In July, a new shopping mall opened on the beltway, and many downtown stores, including those renting space in Danny's building, have either moved or closed. Danny has been unable to rent his stores. Despite offering the building for sale at $70,000, he has been unable to sell it. He received only one offer of $50,000. He has successfully petitioned the property tax valuation administrator to assess the property at $60,000 for local real property tax purposes. What are the tax consequences to Danny of these events?

       (2)   Would your answer be different if the fair market value of the property had fallen to $40,000?

(f)   (1)   Luke Landlord owns an office building with a basis of $100,000 and a fair market value of $200,000. The building is 100 percent occupied under long-term leases that yield gross annual rents of $48,000. On December 31 of last year, Luke

116

sold half of the undivided rents for this year to Ralph Rothschild for $18,000. This year, Luke remitted half of the gross rents to Ralph as they were collected at the rate of $2,000 per month. What are the tax consequences to Luke?

(2)   What are the consequences to Ralph?

(g)   (1)   Paul Portfolio owns 500 shares of IBM stock, which he bought many years ago for $100 per share ($50,000 total cost). The stock is currently trading at $60 per share ($30,000 total). Paul would like a deduction for his $20,000 loss, but he believes IBM stock is now a good investment, so he wants to keep his shares. Being aware of the "hair trigger" approach to realization taken by the Supreme Court in *Cottage Savings*, Paul decides to realize his loss by trading his 500 IBM shares for 500 identical IBM shares owned by Peter. Will this plan work?

(2)   If it won't work, what about Paul selling his shares and then immediately buying identical shares?

(h)   Bank loaned $1 million to Dan Developer to finance Developer's shopping center. The interest rate on the loan was 10 percent. Interest was payable monthly, but principal was payable only upon maturity in twenty years. Two years after the loan was made, the local economy went into a recession, and Developer lost several major tenants, causing major damage to Developer's cash flow. Does the Bank realize gain or loss with respect to the loan in either of the following situations?

(1)   When Developer became a month late on an interest payment, Bank became entitled to declare the loan in default and invoke an acceleration clause (under which payment of principal would be due immediately). In the hopes that Developer would soon find new tenants, Bank temporarily waived the clause.

(2)   Developer and the Bank agreed to modify the loan by reducing the interest rate to 9 percent.

(i)   Denise Dealer is a securities dealer with the following portfolio as of the beginning of 2003 (no part of which was held for investment): 10 shares of X stock with a $50 basis ($5 per share); 20 shares of Y stock with a basis of $800 ($40 per share); and 20 shares of Z stock with a basis of $2,000 ($100 per share). During 2003, she sold 2 shares of X

117

stock for $5 each, 4 shares of Y stock for $25 each, and 5 shares of Z stock for $100 each. At the end of 2003, the stocks were worth the following: X stock was worth $11 per share; Y stock was worth $20 per share; and Z stock was worth $120 per share. How much gain or loss must Denise recognize?

(j)   Paul Program owns 10,000 shares of Microsoft, with a basis of $100,000 and a value of $2 million. He would like to cash out his investment, but he does not want to pay tax on $1.9 million of capital gain. His tax lawyer suggests the strategy of a "short sale against the box." Under this plan, Paul would "borrow" 10,000 Microsoft shares from his broker (pledging his own shares as security), and then sell the borrowed shares on the market for $2 million. Paul would then have $2 million cash, and he would have eliminated all risk with respect to future changes in the value of the stock, because his "long" and "short" positions would exactly offset one another. That is, any decrease in the value of the shares he owns would be offset by a decrease in the value of the shares he must repay. Will this plan give Paul the economic equivalent of a cash sale, without being treated as a realization event?

29

Sales of Property—Basis and Amount Realized

PROBLEM SET 29-1

¶ 29.01 BASIS: IN GENERAL; ¶ 29.02 UNADJUSTED BASIS—COST

(a)   Billy Buyer purchased an apartment building from Sam Seller for $100,000 cash. Billy also promised to pay Sam the lesser of either half the gross rents or all of the net rents received, until he had paid an additional $100,000 (plus interest at 12 percent per year, which was adequate interest at the time of the sale). The debt is evidenced by a promissory note and secured by a mortgage. The building is currently fully occupied, and the annual gross rents are $26,000. What is Billy's basis in the apartment building for purposes of computing accelerated cost recovery system (ACRS) deductions?

(b)   Charles Comp, the vice-president of Monolith Industries, was allowed to purchase from Monolith 10,000 shares of its stock for $200,000. When he purchased the stock, it was trading on the New York Stock Exchange for $40 a share. If Charles sells the stock for $500,000, how much gain must he recognize?

(c)   Last December, when Swampacre was worth $40,000, Paul Pogo paid the owner, Gus Gator, $1,000 for an option to buy Swampacre at any time in the next six months for $39,500. Paul exercised the option in April, when Swampacre had a fair market value of $42,000. What is Paul's basis in Swampacre?

(d)   Lucy Lucky found a diamond ring on the beach that she had appraised at $5,000. If Lucy later sells the ring for $4,000, what is her basis for computing gain or loss?

PROBLEM SET 29-2

¶ 29.03 PROPERTY ACQUIRED BY GIFT; ¶ 29.04 PROPERTY ACQUIRED FROM DECEDENTS—DATE-OF-DEATH BASIS

(a)   (1)   Bertha Bountiful gave her niece Betty 1,000 shares of stock in Conglomerate Corp. Bertha's basis in the stock was $30,000, and its fair market value at the time of the gift was $40,000. How much gain or loss would Betty recognize if she sold the stock for:

            (i) $60,000?
            (ii) $35,000?
            (iii) $25,000?

        (2)   If Bertha's basis in the stock had been $50,000 and she had given the stock to Betty when it had a fair market value of $40,000, how much gain or loss would Betty have recognized if she later sold the stock for:

            (i) $60,000?
            (ii) $35,000?
            (iii) $45,000?

(b)   (1)   If Bertha sold the stock in part (a)(1) to Betty for $35,000, how much gain would Bertha recognize? (Assume the bargain sale has no gift tax consequences.) What would be Betty's basis in the stock?

        (2)   If Bertha sold the stock in part (a)(2) to Betty for $35,000, how much loss would Bertha recognize? What would be Betty's basis?

(c)   What is the reason for the adjustment to basis prescribed by IRC § 1015(d)?

(d)   Mike and Mary Married owned their home, which they had purchased for $20,000, as joint tenants with rights of survivorship. Mike died last year, and the house was appraised at $80,000 for state inheritance tax purposes. No federal estate tax return was filed. Mary sold the house this year and received $78,000 after paying the real estate broker's commission. How much gain or loss must she recognize?

(e)   Sam Shelter purchased an apartment building for $500,000, paying $50,000 in cash and giving a $450,000 nonrecourse mortgage note for the balance. Sam died before making any payments on the principal and devised the building to his son, Bernard. At the time of Sam's death, the building's fair market value was $400,000. What is Bernard's basis in the apartment building?

(f)   (1)   When he died, Uncle Rich bequeathed Shoreacre, his summer home, which had a fair market value of $100,000, to his sister, Prudence, for life, with the remainder to his nephew, Richie. When Uncle Rich died, the fair market value of Prudence's life estate was $60,000, and the fair market value of Richie's remainder was $40,000. How much gain will be recognized by Prudence and/or Richie under the following circumstances:

   (i)   Prudence immediately sold her life estate to Samantha Sister for $50,000.

   (ii)   Richie immediately sold his remainder to Sam Stranger for $50,000.

   (iii)   Prudence and Richie jointly sold Shoreacre to Samantha for $100,000, of which Prudence received $60,000 and Richie received $40,000.

   (iv)   Richie sold his remainder for $180,000 five years later when Shoreacre had increased in value to $200,000, and, because of the passage of time, his remainder interest had increased in value to 90 percent of the value of Shoreacre.

        (2)   How much gain or loss would Samantha Sister recognize if she immediately resold for $52,000 the life estate in Shoreacre that she purchased in part (f)(1)(i)?

(g)   What is the policy justification for the stepped-up (or stepped-down) basis at death provided by IRC § 1014? If you do not find the justification persuasive, how would you change the law?

PROBLEM SET 29-3

¶ 29.07 ALLOCATION OF BASIS; ¶ 29.08 IDENTIFICATION OF PROPERTY SOLD; ¶ 29.09 ADJUSTMENTS TO BASIS; ¶ 29.10 BASIS OF PROPERTY DEVOTED TO PERSONAL USE WHEN SOLD OR CONVERTED TO BUSINESS USE

(a)   Danny Developer purchased Farmacre for $150,000. Farmacre consisted of 133 acres of land, a farmhouse in good condition, and some dilapidated barns. Danny had originally offered O.D. MacDonald, who owned Farmacre, $100,000 for 130 acres, but told MacDonald to keep the farmhouse and the surrounding three acres. MacDonald refused to sell only the unimproved land and demanded $150,000 for the entire tract. Danny agreed. Immediately after purchasing Farmacre, Danny cleared the land and filled swampy areas at a cost of $15,000 (no work was needed on the farmhouse's three acres). He also hired a surveyor and lawyer, at a total cost of $5,000, to obtain approval to subdivide Farmacre into sixty building lots of two acres each and one lot of three acres with the original farmhouse on it. The other ten acres were devoted to roads within the subdivision. Danny immediately sold the farmhouse and three acres for $50,000. Danny began selling the lots, receiving $20,000 for each of the ten lots that had frontage on a small lake bordering the subdivision, and $16,000 each for another ten of the remaining fifty lots (all of which were identical). How much gain has Danny recognized on the sale of the farmhouse and twenty building lots?

(b)   Irene Investor purchased 100 shares of stock in Specific Motors Corp. two years ago for $1,000, and another 100 shares of stock in Specific Motors last year for $2,000. Irene has decided to sell 100 shares of her Specific Motors stock, which is now trading at $15 per share. How will she determine whether she has a $500 gain or a $500 loss?

(c)   Several years ago, Don Duplex bought a parcel of land for $20,000 and built a duplex house on it at a cost of $90,000. Don lived in half of the duplex and rented out the other half. Assuming that Don has properly claimed $13,500 of ACRS deductions on the property,

    (1)   How much gain or loss must Don recognize if he sells the land and duplex this year for $120,000?

(2)   How much gain or loss must Don recognize if he sells the land and duplex this year for $90,000?

(d)   (1)   Several years ago, Vera Vacation purchased for $100,000 an oceanfront cottage that she used exclusively for personal vacations. At that time, $10,000 of the purchase price was allocable to the land, and $90,000 was allocable to the building. The current fair market value of the property is $90,000, of which $10,000 is allocable to the land and $80,000 to the building. If Vera converts the cottage to rental use, what will be her basis for computing ACRS deductions?

        (2)   If Vera claims $10,000 of ACRS deductions and then sells the property, what will be her gain or loss if she sells the property for:
                (i) $120,000?
                (ii) $70,000?
                (iii) $85,000?

PROBLEM SET 29-4

¶ 29.12 AMOUNT REALIZED: IN GENERAL; ¶ 29.13 DEFERRED PAYMENT SALES; ¶ 29.14 PROPERTY OF INDETERMINATE VALUE: "OPEN" TRANSACTIONS; ¶ 29.15 SERVICES AND OTHER BENEFITS AS "AMOUNTS REALIZED"; ¶ 29.16 RELIEF FROM LIABILITY AS AN AMOUNT REALIZED

(a)   Olga Olde owned an antique dining room table for which she had paid $10,000. When the fair market value of the table was $16,000, she traded it to Willie Wheels in exchange for an automobile for which Willie had paid $10,000, and which had an objective fair market value of $14,000. Olga and Willie knew of the disparity in fair market value, but still made the trade. Olga had no intention of making a gift to Willie. How much gain must Olga and Willie each recognize, and what are their respective bases in the car and table after the trade?

(b)   (1)   Gus Gaz owned three of the last remaining independent gas stations in the City of Metropolis. Leviathan Oil Corp., the world's largest corporation, purchased one of Gus's stations last December. At the closing, Leviathan gave Gus a check for $150,000 and an unsecured negotiable promissory note for

$50,000 that bore an adequate rate of interest, with both the interest and principal payable in full one year later. What was the amount realized by Gus on the sale last year? This year?

(2) Gus sold another station to Earl Goober, who just graduated from the local vocational-technical high school. Last December, Earl gave Gus a promissory note for $100,000, with interest at an adequate rate payable annually. The note provides that principal is payable in annual installments equal to 25 percent of Earl's profits and that any unpaid principal is due in full in twenty years. The note was secured by a mortgage on the gas station. This year, Goober paid Gus $20,000. Gus made an election under IRC § 453(d) for IRC § 453(a) not to apply. What is the amount realized by Gus on the sale in the year of the closing? In the next year?

(3) Gus sold his third station to Earl's twin brother Eddie Goober, but under a different arrangement from that in (b)(2). Under this arrangement, the only consideration to Gus is that Eddie obliged himself to pay Gus 40 percent of Eddie's profits from the station for the next twenty years, with no minimum or maximum amount provided for. Eddie's obligation is not secured. Gus made an election under IRC § 453(d) for IRC § 453(a) not to apply. May Gus treat the sale as an open transaction?

(c) Circle Homes, Inc., is in the business of developing subdivisions of hundreds of identical homes. In June of last year, Circle Homes sold to Lois Land, one of its sales representatives, a home for $35,000 that cost Circle Homes $30,000 to build and that normally sells for $50,000. How much income must Circle Homes recognize as a result of this transaction?

(d) (1) Danny Debtor borrowed $10,000 from Cindy Creditor several years ago. Last December, Cindy demanded repayment. Danny had no cash but offered to deed Speculation Acre to Cindy in discharge of the debt. Speculation Acre was an undeveloped tract of land that Danny had purchased several years ago for $6,000. Cindy agreed, and Danny deeded the land to Cindy in December. What are the tax consequences to Danny and Cindy?

(2)   (i)   Suppose, instead, that Danny had offered to transfer to Cindy 100 shares of stock of Monolith Enterprises (in which Danny had a $60 per share basis), which was then trading on the New York Stock Exchange at $100, and Cindy had accepted. However, when the shares were actually transferred the next day, Monolith was trading at only $98 per share. What would be the tax consequences to Danny and Cindy?

       (ii)   How much income would Cindy recognize if she sold the Monolith stock for $110 per share in January?

(e)   (1)   Peter Piper purchased a parcel of land for $20,000 and constructed an apartment building on it at a cost of $380,000. He paid the entire purchase price and construction costs with the proceeds of a nonrecourse loan that was secured by a mortgage on the property. Two years later, when the basis of the apartment building was $340,000 (due to $40,000 of ACRS deductions), the fair market value of the land and building was $500,000, and the outstanding balance on the mortgage was still $400,000, Peter sold the land and building, subject to the mortgage, to Betty Boop for $100,000 in cash. Betty did not expressly agree to assume the mortgage. How much gain must Peter recognize? What is Betty's basis in the building?

      (2)   What would be the tax consequences to Peter if instead of selling the land and apartment building, he deeded it to his daughter, Paula, as a wedding present?

      (3)   What would be your answer if instead of giving the land and apartment building to Paula, Peter died and left it to her under his will?

      (4)   What would be your answer to part (e)(3) if, when Peter died, the fair market value of the land and apartment building were only $300,000? What would be the gain or loss realized by Paula if, immediately after inheriting the apartment building, she deeded it to the mortgagee?

30

Nonrecognition Transactions

PROBLEM SET 30-1

¶ 30.01 NONRECOGNITION OF REALIZED GAIN OR LOSS; ¶ 30.02 EXCHANGES OF PROPERTY FOR PROPERTY OF A "LIKE KIND" → Rule 1031

(a)   Eddie Earl owned an operating oil well with a basis of $50,000 and a fair market value of $200,000. He traded it to Rebecca Rents for $20,000 cash and an apartment house owned by Rebecca that had a fair market value of $180,000. Rebecca's basis in the apartment house was $40,000.

   (1)   How much gain must Eddie recognize? What is his basis in the apartment house?

   (2)   How much gain must Rebecca recognize? What is her basis in the oil well?

(b)   Common Carrier Corp. owned an "18-wheeler" tractor-trailer rig with an adjusted basis of $10,000 and a fair market value of $30,000. If the rig were sold for $30,000, the entire $20,000 gain would be IRC § 1245 recapture gain. The corporation traded the tractor-trailer rig and $30,000 cash to a truck dealer for a new rig that was priced at $60,000. What is Common Carrier's basis in the new rig for purposes of claiming accelerated cost recovery system (ACRS) deductions?

(c)   (1)   Otto Ocean owned a summer cottage with a basis of $50,000 and a fair market value of $100,000. He traded it to Sue Slopes for Sue's ski condominium with a basis of $110,000 and a fair market value of $100,000. Otto and Sue have both previously used the cottage and condominium solely for personal vacation use and will continue to do so after the trade. How much gain or loss must each recognize?

   (2)   What would your answer be if, after the trade, each used the respective property solely for rental?

   (3)   What would your answer be if before the trade Otto had rented his cottage, but after the trade he held the condominium for his personal use?

127

(4)   What would your answer be if Otto had rented the cottage before the trade and rented the condominium after the trade, but Sue had used the condominium and intended to use the beach cottage only for her personal use?

(d)   (1)   Tina Trader owned an apartment building with an adjusted basis of $50,000 and a fair market value of $100,000, which was subject to a mortgage of $30,000. She exchanged the apartment building for one owned by Sam Swap, in which Sam had a basis of $90,000. This building had a fair market value of $120,000 and was subject to a mortgage of $50,000. How much gain must be recognized by Tina and Sam? What are their respective bases in the apartment buildings received?

(2)   (i)   Sam and Tina engage in a second exchange, in which Sam transfers undeveloped land (basis $20,000, and value $70,000) to Tina, in exchange for undeveloped land (basis $30,000, and value $50,000) and IBM stock (basis $15,000, and value $20,000). All the property involved is held for investment, before and after the exchange. What are the tax consequences of this exchange to Sam and Tina?

(ii)   What would be the consequences to Tina if her basis in the stock were $30,000?

(e)   (1)   Danny Developer wanted to buy Fred Farmer's farm to build a shopping center. Fred was hesitant to dispose of his farm, which had a basis of $50,000, unless he could acquire another farm. To induce Fred to sell, Danny persuaded O.D. MacDonald to sell his farm to Fred for exactly the same amount as Danny was willing to pay Fred. Last September 30, Danny, Fred, and O.D. signed a single contract under which Fred agreed to sell his farm to Danny for $100,000, and O.D. agreed to sell his farm to Fred for $100,000. On January 2, Fred gave Danny a deed, and Danny gave Fred a check for $100,000. Fred endorsed the check and gave it to O.D. in exchange for a deed to O.D.'s farm. Must Fred recognize gain?

(2)   Assume instead that Fred deeded his farm to Danny on January 2 in exchange for Danny's promise to buy a farm selected by Fred at a cost of not more than $100,000. Fred located a farm

128

on March 1, a contract between the owner and Danny was signed on March 2, and the farm was deeded to Fred on June 5. Must Fred recognize any gain?

(3)   Now assume that Fred deeded his farm to Danny on January 2 in exchange for the same promise as in part (e)(2), but this time Danny was more prompt. The replacement farm (owned by MacDonald) was located on February 1 and Fred received title on April 1. The events of April 1 were as follows: Danny paid MacDonald $100,000 for the replacement farm, and, at Danny's direction, MacDonald transferred legal title directly to Fred. Thus, Danny never had legal title to the farm. Does this qualify under IRC § 1031 as to Fred?

(f)   For the purpose of asset diversification, Robert James Waller and Rod McKuen agree to an exchange of copyrights—the copyright on Waller's new novel, *The Irrigation Ditches of Madison County*, for the copyright on McKuen's new poetry collection, *Listen to the Lukewarm*. Does the exchange qualify for nonrecognition under IRC § 1031?

(g)   Arlene owned a condominium rental unit with a basis of $100,000 and a value of $250,000. The remaining cost recovery period for the unit, under IRC § 168(c)(1), was fifteen years. She traded it with Bob for a different condo rental unit worth $300,000. To even up the values, Arlene also paid Bob $50,000 cash. What is Arlene's basis in the new unit, and over what length of time will she be allowed to recover that cost? See Prop. Reg. § 1.168-5(f)(2).

PROBLEM SET 30-2

¶ 30.03 GAIN ON INVOLUNTARY CONVERSIONS OF PROPERTY

(a)   (1)   Luke Landlord owned the Tenement Manor, an apartment building that had an adjusted basis of $50,000 and was subject to a mortgage of $80,000. The building was located within the right-of-way of a proposed highway and thus was condemned by the state. Luke received $70,000, and the mortgagee bank received $80,000. Within one year, Luke purchased another apartment building, Slum Gardens, for $140,000, paying

$40,000 in cash and assuming an existing mortgage of $100,000. If Luke elects the benefits of IRC § 1033, how much gain must he recognize, and what will be his basis in the new apartment building?

(2)   What would be your answer to part (a)(1) if the building purchased by Luke were a motel that he planned to operate?

(3)   What would be your answer to part (a)(1) if Luke's apartment building had been burned to the ground and he had received $150,000 of insurance proceeds, which he reinvested in a motel that he planned to operate?

(4)   What would be your answer to part (a)(1) if, for $150,000, Luke purchased all the stock of a corporation, the sole asset of which was an apartment house?

(5)   What would be your answer to part (a)(1) if, for $150,000, Luke purchased 50 percent of the stock of a corporation owning and operating an apartment house?

(6)   What would be your answer to part (a)(1) if, for $150,000, Luke purchased 100 percent of the stock of a corporation owning and operating a motel?

(b)   Tom Ptomaine owned and operated a restaurant that was condemned to make way for an urban renewal project. Tom received $100,000 for his building, which had an adjusted basis of $50,000. He sold all of his restaurant equipment (kitchen equipment, tables, and chairs), which had a basis of zero, for $20,000. Within two years, Tom purchased a bar and dance hall business for $120,000, of which $100,000 was attributable to the building, and $20,000 was attributable to the equipment (bar, refrigeration, tables, chairs, pool tables, video games, and sound system). To what extent may Tom elect nonrecognition under IRC § 1033?

(c)   Ralph Retailer operated a hardware store in a leased building. Last December, the building was totally destroyed by fire. Ralph received insurance proceeds of $110,000, of which $100,000 was attributable to inventory with a basis of $50,000, and $10,000 was attributable to equipment (shelves, cash register, and desk) with a basis of zero. Ralph leased another retail store, but this time he went into the toy business. He paid $20,000 for new equipment (shelves, cash register, and desk) and paid $70,000 for inventory last year. Ralph paid another $70,000 for inventory this year. Last year, Ralph had no sales from his toy business; this year, his sales were $100,000. May Ralph use IRC § 1033 to defer the gain realized when he received the insurance proceeds?

PROBLEM SET 30-3

¶ 30.06 TRANSFERS BETWEEN SPOUSES AND FORMER SPOUSES (SEE ALSO ¶ 28.05)

(a) Willie and Wendy Wander were divorced last December. Pursuant to the divorce, this February Willie transferred 1,000 shares of stock in Leviathan Corp. to Wendy. Willie had purchased the stock in his own name several years before for $50,000. At the time of the transfer, the fair market value of the stock was $60,000. Wendy sold the stock this April for $55,000. What are the tax consequences to Willie and Wendy?

(b) (1) Phil and Paula Philander were divorced last year. Pursuant to the divorce decree, Paula was awarded their house, which they had held as joint tenants. Phil and Paula had purchased the house ten years ago for $50,000; at the time of the divorce, its fair market value was $100,000. Phil was awarded 1,000 shares of stock of Domestic Offices Machine Corp., which they had held as joint tenants. The fair market value of the stock was $100,000, and it had been purchased two years ago for $110,000. This May, Paula sold the house for $105,000, and Phil sold the stock for $105,000. What are the income tax consequences to Phil and Paula of these events?

(2) Would your answer be different if the only asset Phil and Paula had was the house, which was awarded to her and sold by her?

(c) (1) Last December, Mary Money sold 1,000 shares of stock in Monolith Corp. to her husband Mike for $50,000 (which was fair market value). Mary had purchased the stock two years ago for $60,000. Mike sold the stock for $45,000 in January. What are the tax consequences of this transaction?

(2) Would your answer be different if Mary had paid $40,000 for the stock?

      (3)   Would your answer to part (c)(1) be different if Mary had given the stock to Mike as a gift?

(d)   (1)   Steve and Samantha Split were divorced in December 2002. Each received the property that he or she had held in his or her own name. However, as part of the settlement, Steve gave Samantha a right of first refusal if he decided to sell Lakeacre, their summer vacation home that had been awarded to Steve, within the next two years. In 2003, Steve decided to sell Lakeacre and, pursuant to her right of first refusal, Samantha matched an arm's-length offer of $75,000 and purchased the home on November 15, 2003. Steve's basis in Lakeacre was $50,000. What are the tax consequences of this transaction?

      (2)   What would your answer be in part (d)(1), if the sale took place on January 15, 2004?

(e)   Ralph and Ruth Roamer are currently negotiating a divorce settlement. The proposed property settlement would allow Ruth to live in their home, which they own as joint tenants, for ten years rent free (until their youngest child graduates from high school). At any time within those ten years, Ruth may purchase Ralph's half of the house for a price determined under a formula. If Ruth purchases the house at the end of ten years, will Ralph be required to recognize any gain realized on the sale? How will Ruth's basis be determined?

31

Taxation of Capital Gains and Losses—Basic Structure and Definitions

PROBLEM SET 31-1

¶ 31.01 INTRODUCTION; ¶ 31.02 BASIC CAPITAL GAIN/LOSS STRUCTURE

(a)   Before taking capital gains and losses into account, Carla Capital (a single taxpayer) had $400,000 of taxable income last year. What is her taxable income in the situations described below, taking into account capital gains and losses? Does any part of that income qualify for a special rate? In addition, what is her capital loss carryover, if any?

    (1)   Carla recognized a $10,000 short-term capital gain.

    (2)   Carla recognized a $10,000 long-term capital gain on the sale of Microsoft stock she had purchased three years earlier.

    (3)   Carla recognized a $10,000 long-term capital gain on the sale of Microsoft stock that she had purchased in 2001. The sale took place in 2007.

    (4)   Carla recognized a $10,000 long-term capital gain on the sale of porcelain figurines.

    (5)   Carla recognized a $10,000 short-term capital loss.

    (6)   Carla recognized a $10,000 long-term capital loss and a $2,000 short-term capital gain.

    (7)   Carla recognized a $10,000 long-term capital loss, and a $15,000 long-term capital gain on the sale of Microsoft stock she had purchased three years earlier.

    (8)   Carla recognized a $2,000 long-term capital gain, a $1,000 short-term capital gain, a $3,500 long-term capital loss, and a $10,000 short-term capital loss.

PROBLEM SET 31-2

¶ 31.03 BASIC DEFINITION OF "CAPITAL ASSET"; ¶ 31.04 PROPERTY HELD FOR SALE TO CUSTOMERS; ¶ 31.05 PROPERTY USED IN THE TRADE OR BUSINESS; ¶ 31.10 OPTIONS TO BUY OR SELL PROPERTY

(a)   Danny Developer purchased Swampacre, a 1,000-acre tract of unimproved land, five years ago for $1 million. Shortly after the purchase, Danny spent $100,000 to fill swampy areas and obtain approval to subdivide the tract into 500 building sites. For the next two years, Danny developed and sold 200 homes on other land. Three years ago, Danny built homes on and sold 100 lots from Swampacre. For the last two years, Danny has not built and sold homes on his own account, but has acted as a contractor to build apartment buildings for Luke Landlord. Recently, Luke offered to purchase 200 lots of Swampacre Subdivision, which Luke will consolidate to erect an apartment complex. Will Danny be entitled to treat the gain on the sale to Luke as a capital gain? Will the character of Danny's profit-making activities next year be relevant?

(b)   Rebecca Realtor is a real estate broker; she earns most of her income from commissions on homes that she sells as an agent for their owners. Occasionally, when Rebecca sees a home listed by another realtor at a price she considers low, she buys it for her own account and sells it at a higher price. Over the last ten years, Rebecca's average annual commission earnings have been $40,000. She usually buys and sells two or three homes a year on her own, and her average yearly profit from this activity is $25,000. Are Rebecca's profits from buying and selling homes eligible for capital gains treatment?

(c)   Bertha Bigbucks is independently wealthy, and all of her income is derived from investments. Her annual interest and dividend income is $500,000. In addition, she buys and sells shares of portfolio stock regularly in an attempt to earn profits on price fluctuations. Last year she made 150 purchases at an aggregate price of $3 million and sold 100 different issues for $4 million (resulting in a net loss of $400,000). May Bertha treat her losses on the sale of stock as ordinary losses?

(d)   Fred Farmer purchased the 500-acre farm adjacent to his farm six years ago for $400,000, of which $350,000 was paid with the proceeds of a mortgage loan. Fred's purpose in purchasing the adjacent farm was to prevent development of that farm as a subdivision and to expand his own operations. Last year, Fred fell behind on his loan payments. The mortgagee suggested that Fred subdivide and sell some building lots on the far side of the new farm—the lots that were farthest from the border with his old farm. Since the land in question was wooded and rocky, Fred agreed. He obtained subdivision approval for ten lots of four acres each. Fred advertised the lots for sale in the local newspaper, and he sold them all this year for $20,000 each, of which $19,000 represented a gain on each lot. May Fred report these gains as capital gains? (See also ¶ 33.07.)

(e)   Old King Cole Coal Corp. (OKCC Corp.) owned a coal mine that it had operated for many years. Its basis in the coal deposit was $200,000, and its adjusted basis for the associated buildings was $30,000. OKCC Corp. sold the coal mine for $200,000, of which $180,000 was allocated to the coal deposit, and $20,000 was allocated to the buildings. What is the character of OKCC's losses?

(f)   While browsing through the B.B. Legume catalog one day, Hank Hunter conceived the idea that an outdoorsman would like a line of camouflage suits emblazoned with a hanging deer carcass. After some negotiations that lasted more than one year, Hank sold his idea to B.B. Legume, which registered the logo as a trademark. May Hank treat the $20,000 paid to him by B.B. Legume as long-term capital gain? (See also ¶ 31.06.)

(g)   (1)   Irene Investor paid Sandy Seller $10,000 for an option to purchase Niceacre (a parcel of undeveloped land) for $200,000 at any time during the next twelve months. The value of Niceacre never exceeded $180,000 during the option period, so Irene failed to exercise the option. If Irene had exercised the option, she would have held Niceacre for appreciation. May Irene treat the $10,000 cost of the option as an ordinary loss?

           (2)   How should Sandy treat the $10,000 she received from Irene for the option?

(h)   (1)   Sam Snapshot started a camera store twenty years ago and operated it until this year, when he sold his business to Phil Photo for $160,000. The assets of the business, at both adjusted basis and fair market value, that Sam sold to Phil were as follows:

Asset	Adjusted Basis	Fair Market Value
Accounts receivable	$ 10,000	$ 9,500
Inventory	$120,000	$100,000
Furniture	$ 20,000	$ 15,000
Leasehold (5 years left on 10-year lease)	0	$ 5,500
Goodwill	0	$ 30,000

In addition, Phil promised to pay Sam $10,000 per year for Sam's promise not to open a new camera store in the same city during the next three years. What is the amount and character of Sam's gain? (See also ¶ 31.11.)

(2)   Would your answer be different if the title to the assets were held by Sam's Camera Store Corp. and Sam sold all the shares of stock, in which he had a basis of $150,000?

(3)   Suppose the same facts as in part (h)(1), except the agreement signed by Sam and Phil allocates $40,000 to goodwill and nothing to the covenant not to compete. Why might the IRS be suspicious of such an allocation?

(i)   Yolanda has owned a tract of raw land for many years. Her basis in the land is $100,000. She has decided to convert the land into cash, and she has two options. She could simply sell the land to a real estate developer for $1,100,000. Alternatively, she could divide the land into about fifty lots for single family homes, put in roads and sewers, and sell the lots one by one. She estimates that this would involve about $150,000 of development expenses, and that she would then be able to sell the lots for a total of about $1,450,000. After taxes and expenses, will she end up with more cash in her pocket if she sells the raw land to a developer, or if she develops the land herself? Assume that her tax rate on long-term capital gains is 20 percent, her marginal tax rate on ordinary income is 35 percent, and that if she develops the property herself all the lots will be property described in IRC § 1221(a)(1).

PROBLEM SET 31-3

¶ 31.12 JUDICIAL RESTRICTIONS ON CAPITAL GAIN AND LOSS TREATMENT (SEE ALSO ¶ 31.04)

(a) (1) Tammy Trivia, a journalist by profession and an avid reader and board game player, conceived the idea of a game she called Insignificant Chase. The game would be played by moving tokens to different squares on a board following the roll of a die and then answering a question in the category designated on the board. The first player to correctly answer a question in all categories would win. In May, Tammy made a prototype game board and set of question cards and presented the idea for the game to R&S Games, Inc., the nation's leading manufacturer of board games. R&S was impressed by the concept—although its experts wanted to make some changes in the design of the board and the questions—and, after studying the concept for awhile, in December agreed to pay Tammy $500,000 for the rights to the idea (which was not subject to protection under either copyright or patent law). May Tammy treat the proceeds from the sale of the idea as long-term capital gain? (See also ¶ 31.06.)

 (2) Would your answer be the same if Tammy had sold the idea to R&S Games in exchange for 2 percent of gross sales for as long as the game was marketed? (See also ¶ 32.01.)

 (3) If, after producing and selling Insignificant Chase for one year, R&S Games sold the idea to Milty Brady Corp. for $1 million, would the gain recognized by R&S be capital gain?

(b) Leviathan Corp. is a holding company that derives its income principally from dividends paid by its twenty-five subsidiary corporations that operate active businesses. Last January, Leviathan entered into a contract to purchase 100 percent of the stock of Hi Tech, Inc., for $10 million. The closing was set for May 1. The contract provided that Leviathan would be excused from performance if there was a material change in Hi Tech's financial condition prior to the closing. In March, Worldwide Business Products Corp. sued Hi Tech for patent infringement, seeking $5 million in damages. Leviathan's attorneys concluded that Leviathan was entitled to rescind the purchase agreement. Leviathan's management, however, decided to go ahead and close the deal to protect Leviathan's reputation for "square dealing in buying and selling subsidiary corporations." Leviathan purchased Hi Tech for $10 million and immediately began seeking a buyer. On December 31, 100 percent of the stock of Hi Tech was sold for $6 million. Is the loss incurred by Leviathan a capital loss or an ordinary loss?

(c)   Global Airlines spends tens of millions of dollars annually for jet fuel. Because it has very limited storage facilities, it buys fuel only a few weeks before it is to be used. This puts Global at great risk from sudden increases in the price of jet fuel. To hedge against this risk, Global regularly enters into jet fuel futures contracts, requiring it to buy a specified quantity of jet fuel at a specified price at a specified date in the future. Although Global could take delivery under these contracts, more commonly it sells the contracts shortly before the specified date and simply buys the fuel it needs on the market. If the price of fuel has risen unexpectedly, it can sell the contracts at a gain, which offsets the increase in the price it must pay for fuel. Conversely, if the price of fuel oil falls unexpectedly, it sells the contracts at a loss, which offsets the savings from the decrease in the price it pays for fuel. Assuming Global satisfies the identification rules of Treas. Reg. § 1.1221-2(f), are the gains and losses on the sales of the futures contracts ordinary or capital?

(d)   Round-the-Clock Corporation operates a chain of convenience stores, many of which sell gasoline. To ensure a source of gasoline during possible energy crises, Round-the-Clock bought about 30 percent of the stock of NuCorp, an oil and gas exploration and development company. After several years, Round-the-Clock decided the risk of another energy crisis was small, and sold its NuCorp stock at a considerable loss. Is the loss ordinary or capital?

(e)   (1)   Vince Video had owned and operated Vince Video's TV Shoppe for forty years before he retired last year. Just before his retirement, his major competitor, Tommy Tube, offered Vince $100,000 for the right to use Vince's name. Tommy wanted to rename his store Vince and Tommy's Video Tube Shoppe to attract Vince's many loyal customers to Tommy's shop. Vince had no obligation to perform any services. May Vince treat the $100,000 as long-term capital gain?

(2)   If Vince had died while operating the shop and Tommy had paid Vince's widow $100,000 for the right to use Vince's name, could Vince's widow treat the amount as long-term capital gain?

(f)   Prior to his retirement, Vince Video had a contract with the Big City Public School Board to perform service work that paid a guaranteed minimum annual fee of $10,000 on all televisions and videocassette recorder equipment owned by the school board. The contract, which was entered into a year ago, was assignable and had four years to run when Vince retired. If he assigns the contract to Tommy for $15,000, will Vince be entitled to capital gain treatment?

(g)   (1)   Five years ago, Lee Landlord leased a commercial building to Tina Tenant for a term of twenty-five years for an annual rent of $10,000. If Lee assigns the annual rents due under the remaining term of the lease to Ike Investor for $85,000, may Lee treat his gain as long-term capital gain?

(2)   If, one year later, Ike Investor sold to Fran Factor for $90,000 the right to the rentals that he purchased in part (g)(1), may Ike treat his gain as long-term capital gain?

(3)   If Lee sells an undivided half interest in the building for $150,000, must Lee treat $42,500 (half of the present value of the rentals) as ordinary income and only $107,500 as the amount realized on the sale of the interest in the building?

(4)   If Lee pays Tina $40,000 to surrender her lease, which has twenty more years to run, may Tina treat her gain as long-term capital gain? (See also ¶ 32.04.)

(5)   If Tina had sublet the building to Sammie Sublessee three years ago for $12,000 a year, and Sammie paid Tina $17,000 for an assignment of all of Tina's interest in the lease, could Tina have treated her gain as long-term capital gain?

(h)   Paula Portfolio owned 100 shares of stock in Consolidated Conglomerate Corp. (which she purchased two years ago for $50 per share). The stock opened trading on the New York Stock Exchange at $100 per share on August 1. At noon that day, Consolidated announced that on August 10 it would pay a dividend of $4 per share to all shareholders of record as of August 2. Immediately thereafter, Consolidated stock was trading at $104. If Paula sold her Consolidated stock for $104 on August 1, how much of her gain would be capital gain?

PROBLEM SET 31-4

¶ 31.13 CORRELATION WITH PRIOR RELATED TRANSACTIONS

(a)   Fred Fox sold 100 shares of stock in Scamco Corp. to Mike Mark two years ago for $10,000. At that time, Fred reported a capital gain of $9,000. This year, Mike sued Fred for damages in connection with the sale, alleging fraud and violation of state and federal securities laws. Fred paid Mike $8,000 in settlement of Mike's claims. How should Fred treat this transaction on his income tax return?

32

Capital Gains and Losses— "Sale or Exchange" and Holding Period Requirements

¶ 32.01 "SALE OR EXCHANGE" VERSUS "OTHER DISPOSITION"

(a) (1) Edna Equis owned a valuable Arabian horse named Sheik that she purchased eight years ago for $5,000 and used for pleasure riding and showing. Sheik became quite valuable because he had won numerous ribbons. (No prizes other than ribbons were awarded at the shows.) If she had chosen to do so, Edna could have earned substantial amounts by breeding Sheik. With this potential in mind, Edna insured Sheik's life for $25,000. Last year, Sheik cut his leg on a fence and developed an infection. He died nine months later. May Edna report the $20,000 gain she realized when she received the insurance proceeds as long-term capital gain? *

(2) Suppose the same facts as in part (a)(1), except Edna had paid $30,000 for Sheik. Could she then deduct $5,000 as an ordinary loss upon Sheik's death?

(b) (1) Rupert Rich died twenty years ago, leaving his $1 million estate in trust, with the income to be paid equally among his children for the rest of their lives, and the remainder to be divided equally among his grandchildren upon the death of his last surviving child. In addition, each child was entitled to $100,000 in cash or property from the corpus twenty years after Rupert's death. Five years ago, Sam Speculator paid Rupert's daughter Buffy $60,000 for Buffy's right to the $100,000 distribution. This year, the trust satisfied the obligation by distributing to Sam 1,000 shares of stock in Monolithic Industries Corp., worth $100,000, in which the

141

trust had a basis of $60,000. What are the tax consequences of this distribution to Sam and to the trust?

(2) What would have been the tax consequences for Sam if, one month before the distribution from the trust, he had sold to Fred Fox for $99,000 the right he had purchased from Buffy? Would your answer be different if Sam had sold the right three years ago for $75,000?

(3) What will be the tax consequences to the trust when, upon termination, it distributes to Rupert's grandchildren portfolio corporate stock with a basis of $1 million and a fair market value of $2 million?

PROBLEM SET 32-2

¶ 32.03 WORTHLESS SECURITIES

(a) In November of last year, Patsy Portfolio bought 200 shares of stock in Icarus Airlines, Inc., for $2,000. On April 1 of the current year, she sold 100 shares, having a basis of $1,000, for $200. On April 2, Icarus Airlines went into receivership. It was clear by June 1 that the common shareholders would receive nothing from the bankruptcy estate. What is the character of Patsy's loss from these events?

(b) Charlie Close and his four brothers were equal shareholders of Close Corp. Last year, Charlie loaned $10,000 to Close Corp., which Close Corp. used to buy machinery. This year, Close Corp. went bankrupt, and it is clear that Charlie will receive none of the $10,000 owed to him. What is the character of Charlie's loss deduction?

PROBLEM SET 32-3

¶ 32.07 REQUISITE HOLDING PERIOD; ¶ 32.10 "TACKED" HOLDING PERIOD; ¶ 32.11 INHERITED PROPERTY

(a) Irene Investor, a cash method taxpayer, bought and sold stock in the following transactions. What is the amount, character, and year of her gain or loss in each of the following situations?

(1)   On January 31 of last year, she purchased 100 shares of stock in Monolithic Industries, Inc., for $1,000. She sold the shares on January 31 of this year for $1,100.

(2)   On March 31 of last year, she purchased 100 shares of Leviathan Corp. stock for $1,000. She sold the shares on April 1 of this year for $900.

(3)   On November 1, 2003, she purchased 100 shares of Consolidated Conglomerate Corp. stock for $1,100. On February 1, 2004, she purchased another 100 shares for $900. On December 31, 2004, she ordered her broker to sell 100 shares for $1,000, and the broker executed the order. On January 5, 2005, she transferred the shares and received $1,000.

(b)   (1)   On January 1 of last year, Donna Donor purchased 100 shares of stock in Toxic Chemical Corp. for $10,000. In July of this year, when the fair market value of the stock was $9,000, she gave the stock to her daughter, Debbie. Debbie sold the stock in November. What would be the amount and character of her gain if Debbie sold the stock for $11,000?

    (2)   What would be the amount and character of her loss if she sold the stock for $8,000?

(c)   Debbie Decedent purchased 100 shares of stock in Leviathan Corp. for $10,000 on July 1. On October 1, when the stock was worth $11,000, Debbie died. On December 1, her executor sold the Leviathan Corp. stock for $12,000. What is the character of the gain recognized by the estate?

(d)   Willie Wheels purchased a 1956 Dreamobile car at the junkyard on January 1, 2003, for $200 and began restoring it. During 2003, he spent $1,800 on parts and put in hundreds of hours of work on the car in his garage. On December 31, 2003, when restoration work was partially completed, he was offered $4,000 for the car, but declined the offer. During all of 2004, Willie spent an additional $2,000 on parts and also spent many hours working on the car. On January 1, 2005, he sold the car for $8,000 because he was getting married and needed the cash for a down payment on a house. What is the character of Willie's gain?

33

Quasi–Capital Assets and Other Specially Treated Items

PROBLEM SET 33-1

¶ 33.01 QUASI–CAPITAL ASSETS—THE § 1231 HOTCHPOT; ¶ 33.02 INVOLUNTARY CONVERSIONS—THE "PRELIMINARY HOTCHPOT"

(a)   (1)   Lenny Landlord owns approximately fifty duplex housing units that he has rented out for several years. Last year, he sold one duplex, with an adjusted basis of $60,000, for $80,000, and another unit, with an adjusted basis of $75,000, for $50,000. Neither unit had any recapture potential. What is the character of his gain and loss?

       (2)   What would have been the character of the gain and loss if the duplex with a $75,000 basis had been sold for $65,000?

       (3)   What would have been the character of the gain and loss in part (a)(2) if the duplex with the adjusted basis of $60,000 had been held for less than one year?

       (4)   Assuming that the events in part (a)(1) occurred last year, what will be the character of the gain if, this year, Lenny sells for $70,000 a duplex with a basis of $60,000 and a holding period of two years?

       (5)   Assuming that the events in part (a)(2) occurred last year, what will be the character of the loss if, this year, Lenny sells for $70,000 a duplex with a basis of $80,000 and a holding period of two years?

(b)   (1)   Last year, Helen Hotchpot sold for $20,000 an unimproved tract of land, in which she had a basis of $25,000. Helen had been leasing the land to a used car business for several years. Another unimproved tract of land held for speculative investment purposes that had a basis of $10,000 and a holding period of more than one year was condemned by the state for a road project, and Helen received $13,000. In addition,

Helen's home was burglarized, and she received $10,000 of insurance proceeds for the theft of jewelry (which she had owned for several years) that cost $5,000. What is the character of Helen's gain and loss arising from these events?

(2)   What would be the result in part (b)(1) if the $10,000 insurance proceeds were received with respect to the theft of gems held by Helen for speculative investment purposes?

(3)   What would be the result in part (b)(2) if the theft had been of uninsured investment gems?

(c)   Vince Video sold his television store and repair shop business for $200,000. What is the character of his gain if the sales price was allocated among the assets as follows:

Asset	Adjusted Basis	Fair Market Value
Inventory	$60,000	$80,000
Equipment	$20,000	$15,000
Land	$20,000	$25,000
Building	$50,000	$45,000
Goodwill (self-created)	0	$35,000

(d)   Is there any principled defense of the way in which IRC § 1231 lets taxpayers play "heads I win, tails you lose," with the IRS? In other words, why should a net § 1231 gain be capital, while a net § 1231 loss is ordinary?

PROBLEM SET 33-2

¶ 33.04 RECAPTURE OF DEPRECIATION AND OTHER TAX ALLOWANCES

(a)   Confederate Express Corp. operates an airfreight service. Several years ago, it purchased an airplane for use in its business, at a cost of $100,000. This year, it sold the plane. During the time it owned the plane, Confederate Express properly claimed depreciation deductions of $58,000 on the plane. What is the amount and character of its gain or loss if Confederate Express sold the plane for:

    (1) $90,000?
    (2) $110,000?
    (3) $40,000?

(b)   Lisa Lessor purchased a small apartment building in 1997 for $200,000, of which $180,000 was attributable to the building, and $20,000 was attributable to the land. She sold the building several years later for $210,000, of which $190,000 was attributable to the building, and $20,000 was attributable to the land. During the time she owned the building, she had properly claimed $50,000 of depreciation deductions on it, using the straight-line method required by IRC § 168(b)(3)(B). What is the amount and character of Lisa's gain on the sale, and what tax rate will apply to her gain? Assume Lisa has no other § 1231 gains or losses.

(c)   (1)   Sal Monella owns a car that he uses exclusively in his pizza delivery business. Sal paid $12,000 for the car several years ago and has properly claimed $10,000 of depreciation on the car. The car is now worth $5,000. If Sal gives the car to his son, what will be the income tax consequences to Sal? If the son uses the car for personal purposes for two years and then sells it for $3,500, what will be the tax consequences to the son?

        (2)   Assume the same facts as in (c)(1), except Sal donates the car to the Salvation Army. What would be the tax consequences to Sal of this donation?

        (3)   Assume the same facts as in (c)(1), except Sal dies when the car is worth $5,000, and the son inherits the car. What would be the income tax consequences to Sal and his son?

        (4)   Assume the same facts as in (c)(1), except Sal sells the car to an unrelated purchaser for $5,000. The $5,000 consists of $1,000 cash and a $4,000 note (bearing an adequate rate of interest) payable in installments over the next three years. What are the tax consequences of the sale to Sal?

(d)   Midcontinental Truckers owned a fully depreciated truck, for which it had originally paid $20,000. Midcontinental traded in the truck, together with $20,000 of cash, to purchase a bigger used truck. Shortly thereafter, because of an unexpected business reversal, it sold the new truck for $35,000. Midcontinental had claimed $3,000 of depreciation on the new truck. What is the character of the gain recognized by Midcontinental?

PROBLEM SET 33-3

¶ 33.05 TRANSFERS OF DEPRECIABLE PROPERTY BETWEEN RELATED TAXPAYERS

(a)   Suzie Seller inherited a vacation condominium at a ski resort from her mother two years ago, when its fair market value was $100,000. For the last two years, Suzie has used the condominium for vacations. Earlier this year, Suzie got married and sold the condominium to Great Vacations Corp., which is wholly owned by her husband, for $150,000. Great Vacations Corp. plans to lease the condominium on a weekly basis to vacationers in the ordinary course of its business. What is the character of Suzie's gain?

PROBLEM SET 33-4

¶ 33.08 RECHARACTERIZATION OF GAIN FROM FINANCIAL TRANSACTIONS

(a)   Rick Ram bought 100 shares of Microsoft stock on January 1, 2002, for $100,000. On the same day, he agreed to sell it to his broker, Bob, for $115,000 on January 1, 2004. Assuming the "applicable rate" is 5 percent, what will be the amount and character of Rick's gain when he sells the stock to Bob?

34

Assignments of Income

¶ 34.01 TRANSACTIONS BETWEEN RELATED TAXPAYERS: IN GENERAL; ¶ 34.02 ASSIGNMENTS OF EARNED INCOME

(a)   (1)   Mary Manager is employed by Planco Corp. at a salary of $75,000. Under a written plan, Planco Corp. pays college education expenses of up to $5,000 per year for any child of any employee. This year, Mary's son and daughter were both enrolled in college, and each of them received $5,000 from Planco Corp. The money was paid directly to the State University to be applied against tuition, room, and board. Who will be taxed on the $5,000 received by each of Mary's children?

    (2)   (i)   Last year, Mary pledged $12,000 of this year's earnings to Ivy University and executed a document assigning that portion of her salary. Ivy University presented the assignment to Planco Corp., which honored it and paid $1,000 a month directly to Ivy University. Mary's salary check was reduced by $1,000 a month. Should Planco withhold taxes on the payments to Ivy University as if they were paid to Mary?

        (ii)   Would your answer be different if, last year, Mary had disclaimed her right to $12,000 of this year's salary and had asked Planco's board of directors to select and pay $1,000 per month to any charitable beneficiary it considered worthy?

(b)   (1)   Frank Fizz is a 60-year-old physician whose average annual net earnings for the past ten years have been $200,000. Frank's daughter, Phyllis, just finished her medical residency in family practice. She was offered positions with a number of health maintenance organizations at salaries varying between $75,000 and $125,000, but she decided to join her father as a partner in his practice. In their first year, the partnership earned $300,000, which they divided equally. Should this allocation be respected for tax purposes? What factors should be considered in reaching a determination?

(2)   During the second year, Phyllis had a baby and took three months' maternity leave. The partnership again earned $300,000, which they again split equally. As a result of Phyllis's maternity leave, Frank handled 60 percent of the patient load for the entire year, and Phyllis handled 40 percent. During the nine months that they both worked, they handled equal patient loads. Should this allocation be respected for tax purposes? What factors should be considered in reaching a determination? Is your answer different from your answer in part (b)(1)?

(c)   Nora Numbers, a CPA, has agreed to pay her son Stu, a junior majoring in accounting at State University, 75 percent of the amount billed by Nora for any income tax returns prepared by Stu for Nora's clients this year. Nora billed clients $5,000 for tax returns prepared by Stu and paid Stu $3,750. How should this transaction be treated for tax purposes?

(d)   Peter Prof is a professor of electrical engineering at Ivy University. As a condition of employment, all faculty members at Ivy University must agree to pay Ivy University 50 percent of any royalties or other income received from exploiting any patent developed while using university facilities. Last year, Peter was awarded a patent developed from research in the university engineering labs. He licensed the patent to Universal Industrial Machines Corp. and received $50,000 of royalties from the license. Is the $25,000 paid to Ivy University taxable to Peter?

(e)   Paula Punker is a well-known rock musician. Before she began her career as a grunge rock idol, Paula had two children, and she is now considering how to finance their education at the least tax cost. Paula proposes to transfer to her children all of the royalties yet to be earned on last year's hit song "You Look Like a Dead Toad," which she wrote and which is copyrighted in her name. She also wants to give her children the manuscript of her autobiography, which is being written under contract with Scuzz Publishing Co. and is half finished. Paula has received a $10,000 advance. When the manuscript is delivered, it will be copyrighted in Scuzz's name, and Paula will receive a 15 percent royalty on sales. Will these assignments successfully shift the incidence of taxation on the royalty income to Paula's children?

PROBLEM 34-2

¶ 34.03 TRANSFERS OF INCOME-PRODUCING PROPERTY

(a) Peter Pater owns a building that has been leased to Hi Cal Corp., the nation's largest supermarket chain, for $50,000 a year under a lease that has twenty years to run. Who will be taxed on the rental income under each of the following alternative transactions?

   (1) Peter deeds the building to his son Paul for five years, after which the title reverts to Peter.

   (2) Peter deeds the building to his son Paul for fifteen years, after which the title reverts to Peter.

   (3) Peter deeds an undivided one-half interest in the building to his son Paul.

   (4) Peter deeds an undivided one-half interest in the building to his son Paul, but Peter retains the sole right to determine to whom the building will be rented or sold, the rental or sales price, and the right to determine whether rents received will be used for repairs or improvements.

(b) (1) On January 2, Peter Pater executed a contract to sell the building in part (a) to Hi Cal Corp. for $500,000. Peter's basis in the building was $200,000. On January 3, Peter deeded the building to Paul. For six months, until the closing, Hi Cal paid Paul $25,000 of rent. At the closing in July, Hi Cal paid Paul $500,000 for the building. How much income must Peter and Paul each recognize?

   (2) Would your answer be different if Peter had negotiated the terms of the sale with Hi Cal before deeding the building to Paul, and Paul, in turn, had signed the contract to sell to Hi Cal?

(c)   (1)   Irene Investor owned 1,000 shares of stock of Bullseye Corp., in which she had a basis of $10,000. On July 1, Leviathan Corp. announced a tender offer by which it would acquire for $50 per share all shares of Bullseye tendered before August 31. On July 31, Leviathan Corp. announced that 85 percent of the shares of Bullseye had been tendered and that, after the purchase was consummated, Leviathan planned to merge Bullseye Corp. into Leviathan, paying the minority shareholders cash. In early August, Irene transferred her shares of Bullseye to her son Ike, who tendered the shares to Leviathan and received $50,000. Who should be taxed on the gain?

        (2)   Would it make any difference if Leviathan had never made the July 31 announcement in part (c)(1)?

(d)   (1)   On December 1, Great Gizmo Corp. declared a dividend of $10 per share payable on December 31 to all owners of record on December 5. On December 2, Sandra Shareholder gave 100 shares of Great Gizmo to her adult daughter, Suzie. Who will be taxed on the $1,000 dividend received by Suzie on December 31?

        (2)   What would be your answer in (d)(1) if Sandra had given the shares to Suzie on December 6?

PROBLEM SET 34-3

¶ 34.04 RECHARACTERIZATION OF NO-INTEREST AND BELOW-MARKET INTEREST LOANS

(a)   (1)   On January 1, 2003, Winthrop Welloff loaned his son, Winky, $10,000, payable on demand, but with no interest. Winky used the proceeds of the loan as a down payment on a house. Winthrop had withdrawn the funds from a mutual fund that was yielding 11 percent interest per year. Winky's only investment income for 2003 was $150 interest on his checking account. The applicable federal rate for all of 2003 was 10 percent. What are the income tax consequences for Winthrop and Winky in 2003?

(2)   Would your answer be different if the amount of the loan were $20,000?

(3)   Would your answer for part (a)(1) be different if Winky had used the $10,000 to purchase 100 shares of Domestic Office Machines Corp., which paid a $750 dividend for 2003, and Winky had also earned $150 of interest on his checking account, but had no other investment income?

(4)   Would your answer be different if Winthrop had loaned Winky $20,000, which Winky then invested in 200 shares of Domestic Office Machine Corp., which paid a $1,500 dividend in 2003?

(5)   Would your answer to part (a)(4) be different if the amount of the loan were $200,000, and Winky had invested it in 2,000 shares of Domestic Office Machines Corp., which paid a $15,000 dividend in 2003?

(b)   On January 1, 2003, Beverly Bucks loaned her daughter, Buffy, $200,000, with principal payable on demand, and 7 percent interest payable annually. The applicable federal rate at the time of the loan and throughout 2003 was 12 percent. During 2004, the applicable federal rate was 11 percent. Buffy invested the $200,000 in a certificate of deposit that earned $20,000 of interest in 2003 and $22,000 of interest in 2004. Buffy made the interest payments when due but made no principal payments. What are the tax consequences to Beverly and Buffy?

(c)   (1)   Charley and Cheryl Close own all of the stock of Close Corp., which manufactures gizmos. Charley is also the president of Close Corp.; his annual salary is $75,000. Charley was invited to join a partnership to invest in some undeveloped land that a friend of Charley's discovered for sale at a bargain price. Lacking the necessary funds to invest, on January 1, Charley borrowed $20,000 from Close Corp. On the advice of his accountant, Charley signed a promissory note payable on demand of the corporation, but bearing no interest. Throughout the taxable year, the applicable federal rate was 10 percent. What are the tax consequences to Charley and to Close Corp. for the year the loan was made?

(2)   How might your answer be different if the amount of the loan were $10,000?

(3)   Would your answer to part (c)(1) be different if the promissory note were payable two years from the date of the loan and the loan were made on December 31?

36

Alimony and Separate Support Payments

PROBLEM SET 36-1

¶¶ 36.01–36.09 (THE ENTIRE CHAPTER)

(a) (1) Willie and Wanda Wayward were divorced last year. Following a contested hearing on July 1, the court entered a decree awarding Wanda alimony of $5,000 a year for four years (but ceasing with her death, if she should die within the next four years). Last year, Wanda received $2,500, and this year she received $5,000. Must Wanda include the payments in income? May Willie deduct them?

(2) Would your answer be different if the divorce decree awarded Wanda alimony of $5,000 a year for four years and was silent regarding the effect of her death (but, under state law, her right to alimony would terminate upon her death)?

(3) What would be your answer to part (a)(1) if the decree specified that the payments to Wanda were in discharge of her claims to marital property used in Willie's business?

(4) Would your answer to part (a)(1) be different if Willie and Wanda had not divorced, but had legally separated pursuant to a decree of separate maintenance and had established separate households, and the payments were pursuant to the decree of separate maintenance?

(5) How would your answer in part (a)(1) be different if the decree provided that if Wanda died within four years, for the remainder of the four years Willie would pay $4,000 per year into a trust for their minor child, Windy?

(6) How can Willie and Wanda draft an agreement under which Willie will pay Wanda $5,000 a year for the rest of her life, but which will result in Wanda not being required to include the payment in gross income and Willie being taxed on the payments?

(b)   (1)   Carl and Candy Cheater were divorced last year. Under a stipulation incorporated in the decree, Carl was required to pay Candy $60,000 last year, $30,000 this year, and $10,000 next year. Assuming that all payments are made when due, what will be the tax consequences to Carl and Candy for each year?

        (2)   What would your answer be in part (b)(1) if the required payments were $37,500 on December 31 of last year, $30,000 on January 1 of this year, and $15,000 on January 1 of next year?

(c)   (1)   Peter and Paula Parent were divorced last year. Paula was awarded alimony of $800 a month for fifteen years or until her death. Peter was also required to pay Paula $200 a month for the support of each of their two children, who were 5 and 9, of whom Paula had custody, until each of the children reached 18. How should the payments from Peter to Paula be taxed to each of them?

        (2)   Would your answer to part (c)(1) be different if Paula were awarded alimony of $1,200 a month until the oldest child turned 18, $1,000 a month until the second child turned 18, and $800 a month thereafter?

        (3)   Would your answer to part (c)(1) be different if Paula were awarded alimony of $1,200 a month until the oldest child turned 18, $1,000 a month until the second child turned 18, and nothing thereafter?

        (4)   Would your answer to part (c)(1) be different if Paula were awarded alimony of $1,200 a month for the next nine years, $1,000 a month for the following four years, and $800 a month thereafter?

(d)   (1)   Ralph and Ruth Roamer were divorced last year. The divorce decree required that Ralph continue to pay the monthly rent of $500 on Ruth's apartment for three years and that he maintain the health insurance coverage on both Ruth and their minor son, Randy (of whom Ruth has custody). The medical insurance costs Ralph $600 per year. How should Ralph's payments be treated by Ralph and Ruth?

        (2)   How would your answer to part (d)(1) be different if the $500 payment was a mortgage payment on a house owned by Ralph,

        but lived in by Ruth? What if Ruth owned the house?

(3)   Ralph paid his lawyer $1,000 for the divorce proceedings and paid Ruth's lawyer $1,200. How should these payments be treated for tax purposes?

(e)   Stan and Sally Split were divorced in January 2002. The divorce instrument required Stan to pay Sally alimony of $20,000 per year for the next ten years or until Sally's death, whichever comes first. Stan paid the alimony in cash according to schedule in 2002 and 2003. In 2004, however, Sally agreed to accept $20,000 worth of Microsoft stock (in which Stan had a $12,000 basis) instead of cash alimony, and Stan transferred the stock to Sally accordingly. What are the tax consequences of this transfer?

(f)   Barney and Betty have been happily married for years, except for some dissatisfaction with their income tax situation. Barney is an executive with a salary of $200,000; Betty is a full-time homemaker with no income. They have now decided to become legally separated under a decree of divorce, solely for tax reasons. They plan to continue to live after the divorce just the same as before, sharing the same house. Pursuant to the divorce decree, Barney will pay Betty $100,000 alimony each year. What tax advantage are they hoping to achieve? Will they succeed?

(g)   Would you favor repeal of IRC §§ 71 and 215? Why or why not?

37

Reallocation of Income and Deductions Between Related Taxpayers

PROBLEM SET 37-1

¶¶ 37.01–37.04 (THE ENTIRE CHAPTER)

(a)   Ellie Entrepreneur owned all ten shares of voting common stock of Great Gizmo Corp., and, for several years, she was paid a salary of $200,000 per year for her full-time work as the corporation's president. Two years ago, Ellie caused Great Gizmo Corp. to issue a tax-free stock dividend of ninety shares of nonvoting common stock. Using the Uniform Gifts to Minors Act, Ellie gave thirty shares of nonvoting stock to each of her three minor children (who were 14, 15, and 16 years old). Last year, although the earnings of Great Gizmo Corp. were up, Ellie decreased her salary by $120,000, and the board of directors of Great Gizmo Corp. (Ellie, her husband, and her certified public accountant (CPA), Nick Numbers) voted to pay a dividend of $1,200 on each share of stock. Each child received $36,000 of dividends. Ellie received $80,000 of salary and $12,000 of dividends. The Commissioner has asserted that all $200,000 should be taxed to Ellie. Is the Commissioner correct? If the Commissioner is correct, what are the tax consequences to Great Gizmo Corp?

38

Grantor Trusts

¶ 38.01 GENERAL PRINCIPLES; ¶ 38.02 TRUSTS WITH REVERSION TO GRANTOR; ¶ 38.03 REVOCABLE TRUSTS

(a)   (1)   Sally Settlor transferred $50,000 to the Last National Bank in trust to pay the income to Sally's adult son, Steve, for twenty years, with a reversion to Sally (or her estate) at the end of that period. Last year, the trust earned $5,000 of interest by investing the corpus. Is any or all of the trust income taxable to Sally?

        (2)   Would your answer be different in part (a)(1) if the term of the trust was thirty-five years?

        (3)   Would your answer be different in part (a)(1) if, instead of a reversion to Sally, at the end of twenty years the corpus was to be distributed to Sally's husband Sam?

        (4)   The facts are the same as in part (a)(3), except that two years after the trust was created, Sam and Sally get a divorce. Will Sally be taxed on the trust income in post-divorce years?

        (5)   Ten years after establishing the thirty-five-year trust in part (a)(2), Sally contributed another $20,000 at a time when the trust corpus was $60,000. The entire $80,000 corpus was invested in a certificate of deposit that earned $8,000 interest. How much of the trust income will be taxed to Sally?

        (6)   Fifteen years after establishing the thirty-five-year trust in part (a)(2), Sally extended its term by five years. Will the trust income be taxed to Sally following this extension?

        (7)   The thirty-five-year trust that Sally Settlor established in part (a)(2) last year earned $4,000 of dividends and $1,000 of long-term capital gains. The dividends were distributed to Steve, but the capital gains were reinvested in corpus subject to reversion to Sally. How much of the trust income must Sally include?

(b)   Grandma Moses transferred $50,000 to the Last National Bank to a trust for the benefit of her grandson, Joseph, who was 15 years old at the time of the transfer. The trust was to distribute all of its income to Joseph annually until Joseph's twenty-first birthday, at which time the trust would terminate, distributing all of its assets to Joseph. However, if Joseph died before reaching 21, all trust assets would revert to Grandma Moses (or her estate). The trust had $5,000 of income last year. Must Grandma Moses include the $5,000 in her income?

(c)   Daddy Dogmatic transferred $1 million to the Last National Bank in trust. Under the terms of the trust, all trust income was to be paid annually to Daddy's daughter, Clara (who was 25 years old and unmarried at the creation of the trust), for the duration of Clara's life. Upon Clara's death, the trust assets would be distributed to her descendants living at her death, or to charity in the absence of any descendants. However, the trust instrument also provided for a complete reversion to Daddy (or his estate) if at any time Clara should marry "outside her faith." This provision was valid under state law. Will Daddy be taxed on the trust's income?

PROBLEM SET 38-2

¶ 38.03 REVOCABLE TRUSTS; ¶ 38.04 USE OF TRUST INCOME FOR GRANTOR'S BENEFIT; ¶ 38.06 POWER TO CONTROL BENEFICIAL ENJOYMENT

(a)   Gary Grantor transferred $100,000 to Last National Bank as trustee for the benefit of Gary's daughter, Gina, for life, with the remainder to go to Gina's children. Gina was 25 years old and unmarried at the time of the transfer. Gary retained the power to revoke the trust if Gina married anyone not of her own religion. This condition was valid under state law. Will Gary be taxed on the trust income?

(b)   Samantha Settlor established a trust, naming Last National Bank as trustee, for the benefit of her daughter, Suzie, for life, with the remainder to go to Suzie's adult child, Sally. Last year, the trust earned $10,000 of income, all of which was distributed to Suzie. What portion of the trust income will be taxed to Samantha under the following alternative terms of the trust?

(1)   Samantha may revoke the trust with the consent of Suzie.

(2)   Samantha may revoke the trust with the consent of Sally.

(3)   Samantha may revoke the trust with the consent of Suzie's husband.

(4)   Samantha may revoke Suzie's income interest in the trust with the consent of Sally. For this part of the problem, assume that in addition to the $10,000 of ordinary income distributed to Suzie, the trust also earned $5,000 of capital gains accruing to corpus.

(c)   (1)   Al Aged transferred $200,000 to the Last National Bank as trustee to pay the income among Al's three children in such portions as the trustee determined to be "in their best interest." When the last child died, the remainder was to go to Al's grandchildren. Will any portion of the trust income be taxed to Al?

(2)   Would your answer to part (c)(1) be different if the trustee could use income to support Al, if it determined that Al's income from other sources was insufficient to provide for his needs?

(3)   How would your answer to part (c)(1) be different if the trustee could distribute corpus to support Al if it determined that Al's income from other sources was insufficient to provide for his needs?

(d)   Grandma Generous deposited $2,000 in a passbook savings account in the Prudent Savings & Loan Association. The passbook was issued in the name of "Grandma Generous, in trust for Ginny Generous." Ginny is Grandma's 3-year-old granddaughter. Grandma put the bank book in her safe-deposit box, planning to give it to Ginny as a surprise birthday present when Ginny turned 18. Who must include in income the interest earned annually on the savings account?

(e)   Danny Deal purchased an apartment building for $200,000 by paying $50,000 in cash and giving the seller a recourse note for $150,000. Ten years later, when the balance due on the promissory note was $100,000, Danny gave the apartment building, subject to the mortgage, to a trust for the benefit of his adult son, Dennis. Over the next ten years, the trustee applied $200,000 of trust income to pay interest and principal to discharge the mortgage lien. Who will be taxed on the income applied to pay the debt?

(f)   Several years ago, Peter Prepp transferred $200,000 to Nell Numbers, his CPA, in trust for the benefit of his daughter, Buffy. Peter has no reversion in the trust. Last year, the trust earned $16,000 of income. The trustee paid $4,000 for Buffy's private high school tuition, $2,000 for her tennis and skiing lessons, $8,000 for a car for her sixteenth birthday, and $2,000 of expenses for a European tour with her high school senior class. Will any of this income be taxed to Peter? Would it make a difference if Peter had recommended to Nell each of the payments to be made?

PROBLEM SET 38-3

¶ 38.01 GENERAL PRINCIPLES; ¶ 38.06 POWER TO CONTROL BENEFICIAL ENJOYMENT

(a)   (1)   Sam Settlor established a single trust for the benefit of his two adult children, Tom and Tina. The income is payable to Tom and Tina in such proportions as the trustee "deems appropriate" for the next twenty years. At the end of twenty years, the corpus is to be distributed equally to Tom and Tina or their estates. Will Sam be taxed on the income of the trust if Sam's wife is the trustee?

          (2)   Will Sam be taxed on the income if the trustee is the Last National Bank?

          (3)   Will Sam be taxed on the income if the trustee is Linda Lawyer, an associate in the law firm in which Sam Settlor is the senior partner?

(b)   (1)   Would your answers in parts (a)(1) and (a)(3) be different if the income was to be distributed to the children equally, "unless the trustee determines that it is necessary to distribute a greater portion to one child to provide necessities of life, such as food, shelter, clothing, and health care"?

          (2)   Who would be taxed on the trust income if corpus, but not income, were distributable under the same standard?

(c)   (1)   Gene Grantor established a trust for the benefit of his four-year-old grandson Georges, naming himself as trustee. Under the terms of the trust, the trustee is to spend trust income for the benefit of Georges or to accumulate income, as the trustee decides is in Georges's best interests. On Georges's twenty-fifth birthday, he will receive the corpus and all accumulated income. If Georges dies before then, the corpus and all accumulated income will be payable in equal shares to three of Gene's other grandchildren—Gail, Gregg, and Geoff (or their estates). Will Gene be taxed on the income that the trust accumulates before Georges's twenty-fifth birthday or on the income the trust distributes?

          (2)   Would your answer to part (c)(1) be different if Gene retained the power to name which of his other grandchildren would receive the trust corpus and accumulated income if Georges died before his twenty-fifth birthday?

(d)   Tina Trustor established a trust for the benefit of her adult daughter, Tammy, for life, with the remainder to be distributed to Tammy's children on her death. Tina named herself as trustee and retained the power to accumulate income or distribute corpus to Tammy without regard to any standard. To what extent is Tina taxable on the trust income?

PROBLEM SET 38-4

¶ 38.01 GENERAL PRINCIPLES; ¶ 38.08 NONGRANTORS WITH POWER TO DEMAND TRUST INCOME OR CORPUS—"MALLINCKRODT TRUSTS"

(a)   When Paul Planner died, his will established two trusts, one for the benefit of each of his adult children, Peter and Patty. Each trust received $200,000 under Paul's will. Under the terms of the trusts, income and corpus are distributable to the life beneficiary in such amounts as the trustee determines appropriate to secure the beneficiary's "happiness." The remainder is distributable to the life beneficiary's estate. Paul's will named Patty the trustee of the trust for Peter's benefit, and Peter the trustee of the trust for Patty's benefit. Last year, each trust had income of $20,000, and each trust distributed $10,000 of income to the beneficiary. Who will be taxed on the income earned by the trusts?

39

Tax Accounting Methods

¶ 39.01 BASIC PRINCIPLES; ¶ 39.02 CASH RECEIPTS AND DISBURSEMENTS METHOD

(a) Larry Landowner leased Greenacre to Wendy Woods, who used Greenacre to operate a summer camp for children and, in the winter, a Nordic ski area. Both Larry and Wendy are calendar-year, cash method taxpayers. The lease requires an annual rental of $2,000, due in arrears on December 31. What are the tax consequences to each of them of the following alternative rental payments?

   (1) Wendy mailed the check on December 30, and Larry received it on January 2.

   (2) On December 30, Wendy went to Larry's office with a check that Larry refused to accept, telling Wendy to mail it. She did, and he received the check on January 2.

   (3) Wendy telephoned Larry on December 31 and informed him that she had written the check, but could not get away from the ski lodge, and that he could pick it up if he desired. Larry did not pick up the check. Wendy mailed it on January 2, and Larry received it on January 5. Does it matter where Larry was when he received the telephone call?

   (4) Wendy hand-delivered the check to Larry's office at 10:00 P.M. on December 30. Larry was not at his office, so Wendy dropped it through the mail slot. Larry found the check on January 2.

   (5) What would be your answer to part (a)(2) if, when Wendy proffered the check, Larry suggested that they amend the lease to change the due date of the rent to January 2, effective with the next rental payment due; Wendy agreed; they amended the lease; and Wendy returned on January 2 with the rental payment?

   (6) How would you answer parts (a)(1) and (a)(2) if the lease required that rent be paid in advance on January 1?

(7)   If the lease were for five years and required a rent payment of $5,000 at execution plus an additional $2,000 per year rental, how should the $5,000 paid on the execution of the lease be treated by each party?

(8)   How would your answer in part (a)(7) be different if $3,000 of the initial payment were to be returned to Wendy upon her surrender of the premises and with the condition that she had not cut and removed any timber?

(b)   Peter Plumber repaired some plumbing in an apartment house owned by Tom Tenement on December 15. Tom paid the $250 bill by charging it to his Master Vista bank card on that day. Peter submitted the receipt to Master Vista on December 28 and was paid on January 5. Tom paid his Master Vista bill on January 10. Both Peter and Tom are calendar-year, cash method taxpayers. In which years should they claim the income and deduction, respectively?

(c)   Paul Painter, who is a self-employed house painter, purchased assorted brushes, paint thinner, drop cloths, and other supplies worth $200 at Ward & Penbuck Department Store on December 28. He paid for the purchase by using his Ward & Penbuck credit card, and he paid his credit card bill on January 10. Paul is a calendar-year, cash method taxpayer. In which year may he deduct the cost of the supplies?

(d)   Amanda holds a winning ticket in the Euphoric State Lottery. As a winner, she is entitled to choose between receiving (1) $100,000 per year for the next twenty years or (2) an immediate one-time payment of $1,100,000. The two options have approximately the same present value. She must make her choice within forty-five days of becoming a winner. If Amanda chooses the first option (the annuity), how will she be taxed?

PROBLEM SET 39-2

¶ 39.01 BASIC PRINCIPLES; ¶ 39.03 ACCRUAL METHOD INCOME; ¶ 39.04 ACCRUAL METHOD EXPENSES

(a)   (1)   Sandy's Soda Shoppe leases space in a commercial building owned by Bill Brick. The lease requires rental payments of

$1,000 per month in arrears on the last day of each month. Both Sandy and Bill are calendar-year, accrual method taxpayers. Sandy paid the December rent on January 2. In what year should Sandy deduct the rent and Bill include the rent in income?

(2)　　If the lease were a five-year lease executed on January 1, at which time Sandy paid Bill $5,000, in addition to the monthly rent of $1,000, when would Sandy deduct and Bill include the $5,000?

(b)　　On January 1, Last National Bank lent $100,000 to Great Gizmo Corp. at an interest rate of 12 percent per year, payable annually in arrears. On December 1, Great Gizmo Corp. filed for reorganization under the bankruptcy law. No interest was paid on December 31, and it is unclear when the interest will be paid, or if it will ever be paid in full. Both taxpayers use the calendar-year method and the accrual method. Must Last National Bank accrue the interest income? May Great Gizmo Corp. accrue an interest deduction?

(c)　　In January, Willie Wrench repaired a delivery truck owned by Alex's Appliance Co. and submitted a bill for $1,000. Alex's Appliance Co. paid $400, but refused to pay the balance because it alleged that not all of the repairs had been done in a workmanlike manner. In February, Alex's Appliance Co. decided that none of the repairs had been properly done and demanded a refund of the $400 that it had already paid. Soon thereafter, it filed a suit for $400, based on breach of contract, which is still pending. Both Willie Wrench and Alex's Appliance Co. are calendar-year, accrual method taxpayers. To what extent must Willie Wrench currently include the $1,000 bill in income, and to what extent may Alex's Appliance Co. deduct it?

(d)　　(1)　　Dennis Driver sued Specific Motors Corp. for $2 million, alleging that he had been paralyzed as a result of an automobile accident caused by a design defect. Specific Motors, which is an accrual method taxpayer, settled the suit by agreeing to pay Dennis $50,000 per year for the next thirty years. Specific Motors chose not to fund its liability, but if it had chosen to do so, the cost of an annuity paying $50,000 annually for thirty years would have been $471,345 (reflecting a discount rate of

10 percent). Specific Motors is in the 35 percent tax bracket. When may Specific Motors accrue the deduction for the $1.5 million damage settlement?

(2)   Would the answer to part (d)(1) be different in the absence of the economic performance rules of IRC § 461(h)?

(e)   Aqua Pool Corp. builds in-ground swimming pools. The price of the deluxe model pool is $25,000, which includes two annual maintenance visits by Aqua Pool personnel for five years after installation. The visit in the spring is for routine opening maintenance, and the one in the fall is for closing maintenance. Customers who do not purchase a deluxe model must pay $100 per service visit, of which $25 is profit and $75 is expense for Aqua Pool. When Aqua Pool sells a deluxe model pool, how should it account for the $1,000 of price that is attributable to maintenance services and the $750 of expenses that it estimates would be attributable to those services if performed currently?

(f)   Atlantic and Pacific Trucking Corp. is a common carrier using the calendar-year, accrual method. Shippers and consignees using A&P Trucking have thirty days after delivery to file claims for goods damaged in transit. It is the policy of A&P Trucking either to allow or reject such claims within thirty days after receipt. Based on twenty years of experience, A&P estimates that it pays $1 for every $10 claimed. At the end of last year, filed claims in the amount of $250,000 were still pending. In addition, A&P estimated that claims in the amount of $150,000 would be filed in January with respect to December shipments. May A&P Trucking accrue a deduction of $25,000 with respect to the filed claims pending as of the end of the year? May it accrue a deduction of $15,000 with respect to the claims it expected to be filed in January?

(g)   McBurger King, Inc., is an accrual method taxpayer operating a national chain of fast food restaurants. During the last few months of 2002, every McBurger King customer received a numbered lottery ticket. On December 31, 2002, McBurger King held a nationally televised drawing, at which a number corresponding to the number of a particular lottery ticket was selected. The holder of that lottery ticket was entitled to a prize of $1 million in cash, upon presentation of the ticket at any McBurger King restaurant. As it happened, the holder of the ticket presented it on January 2, 2003, and received the $1 million check on January 5. May McBurger King deduct the $1 million prize in 2002?

PROBLEM SET 39-3

¶ 39.05 AMOUNTS OWED BY ACCRUAL METHOD TAXPAYERS TO RELATED CASH METHOD TAXPAYERS

(a)   Charley Close and his three brothers each own 25 percent of the stock of Close Corp. Close Corp. is a calendar-year, accrual-method taxpayer, and Charley is a calendar-year, cash method taxpayer. Two years ago, Charley lent Close Corp. $25,000 at 10 percent interest for five years. The first year, interest was paid as due. Last year, the interest for the first six months was paid as due, but during the last half of the year, Close Corp. experienced unexpected losses and was unable to pay Charley $1,250 of interest due on December 31. Payment was finally made the following May. What are the tax consequences of these events?

(b)   Would your answer to part (a) be different if, on December 31, Charley had lent Close Corp. $1,250, which it used to pay him the interest?

(c)   Would your answer to part (a) be different if, on December 31, Close Corp. gave Charley a promissory note, bearing adequate interest, in the face amount of $1,250?

PROBLEM SET 39-4

¶ 39.06 INVENTORIES

(a)   (1)   Earlier this year, Wally Wizard, whose regular job is as a manager of a video arcade, started a new part-time business, purchasing, reconditioning, and selling used pinball machines, operating out of his basement. During the year, Wally purchased twenty machines for $100 each, spent $150 for parts and labor to recondition each machine, and delivered twelve of the machines to customers at a price of $500 each. As of December 31, he had been paid for eight of the machines. Wally, who is a calendar-year, cash method taxpayer, has requested your advice regarding how he should report the receipts and expenses incurred in his pinball machine business on his tax return. Please advise him. In particular, explain how his tax consequences will differ depending on whether or not he elects to take advantage of Rev. Proc. 2000-22, 2001-1 CB 1008.

(2)   How would your advice be different if Wally had paid $50 for five of the pinball machines in January, $100 for ten of the pinball machines in July, and $150 for five of the pinball machines in September, incurred the same $150 expense per machine for reconditioning, and used the first-in, first-out (FIFO) inventory method? Assume that Wally did not make an election under Rev. Proc. 2000-22.

(3)   How would your answer to part (a)(2) be different if Wally used the last-in, first-out (LIFO) inventory method? Again, assume no election under Rev. Proc. 2000-22.

(4)   Is there any method other than LIFO or FIFO available to Wally?

(b)   Should an automobile dealer be allowed to use either LIFO or FIFO to compute income from the sale of automobiles, or must the dealer use the specific asset method?

(c)   Why should taxpayers maintaining inventories be permitted to use the lower of cost or market method of valuing inventory, when investors may not deduct unrealized decline in value of capital assets held for investment?

(d)   On December 30, Flim Flam Shim Co. ordered $250,000 of shims from Shimco Manufacturing Corp., and they were shipped by Shimco on December 31. Flim Flam Shim received the shims on January 3 and promptly paid the invoice. On December 30, Flim Flam Shim shipped $25,000 worth of shims (its inventory amount) to Retail Shim Store Co. It sent the invoice that same day. The shims were delivered by common carrier on January 2, and Flim Flam Shim was paid on January 10. Flim Flam Shim, which is a calendar-year taxpayer, had a physical inventory of $50,000 of shims on hand on December 31. What is Flim Flam Shim Co.'s closing inventory?

(e)   Barrel Bottom Brewing Corp. manufactures and sells beer. A substantial amount of its sales volume is draft beer. Draft beer is sold to distributors in fifteen-gallon aluminum barrels. Barrel Bottom Brewing pays $4 per barrel to purchase them and charges customers a $5 deposit for the barrel, in addition to the $20 charge for the beer. The deposit is refunded to any distributor who returns a barrel in good condition, without regard to whether the barrel was attributable to beer sold to the distributor. Experience indicates that 90 percent of the barrels are returned undamaged. How should Barrel Bottom Brewing treat the deposits and refunds on the barrels for tax purposes?

(f)   Peter Plumber, who has previously been a salaried maintenance employee at a large factory, is planning to establish a plumbing business to serve the home repair market. He expects to gross about $60,000 in his first year; $50,000 will probably be attributable to services, and $10,000 will be attributable to sales of miscellaneous plumbing fixtures, such as faucets, most of which will be installed incidental to repairs. Peter expects to have annual cash expenses for office/shop rental, telephone, advertising, and the like, of $10,000. He expects to spend about $7,000 for a supply of plumbing parts this year, although he will sell only about $5,000 of parts (at the $10,000 retail price described above). Advise Peter regarding the tax accounting methods that he should use.

40

Nonqualified Deferred Compensation, Individual Retirement Accounts, and Other Educational Savings Incentives

PROBLEM SET 40-1

¶ 40.01 INTRODUCTION; ¶ 40.02 DEFERRED COMPENSATION ARRANGEMENTS

(a)   In 2002, Jack Jox signed a ten-year contract to play football for the San Angeles Faultlines of the World Indoor Football League. His complex compensation package is as follows: Upon signing, Jack received $250,000 in cash, and the Faultlines paid Rock of Ages Insurance Co. $250,000 for a single-premium annuity policy that would pay Jack $30,000 a year for the next twenty years. In addition, the Faultlines promised to pay Jack an additional $250,000 in cash and to purchase a second, identical annuity policy when he reported to training camp in 2003. If Jack made the team after training camp (a virtual certainty), the Faultlines would pay Jack a bonus of $200,000, and he would also receive a salary of $250,000 for 2003 and each of the next nine years, even if he did not play for the team in any succeeding year. Jack went to training camp and made the team. When must Jack include the various payments in his income, and when may the Faultlines claim deductions for the payments?

(b)   Edith Exec's employment contract with Leviathan Corp. entitles her to an annual salary of $200,000. In addition, each year Leviathan Corp. must either pay Edith an additional $100,000 or deposit $100,000 into an escrow account with the Last National Bank to fund an annuity for Edith whenever she chooses to retire. For each year, Edith must make her election before January 1 of the year in which the payment will be made. Will Edith be required to include currently the payments to Last National Bank? The interest earned on the account? Why? How could Edith's contract be amended to defer taxation? What are the disadvantages of deferring taxation?

175

(c)   (1)   Section 457 imposes rules for nonqualified deferred compensation of employees of governments and tax-exempt organizations that are much more restrictive than the rules for other employees. Why do you suppose Congress thought this was appropriate?

        (2)   Does the policy behind IRC § 457 suggest similar rules should be extended to employees of certain other employers? If so, which ones?

PROBLEM SET 40-2

¶ 40.03 TRANSFERS OF PROPERTY FOR SERVICES; ¶ 40.04 EMPLOYEE STOCK OPTIONS

(a)   (1)   Patty Program, who previously worked for World Wide Computer Corp., recently moved to Hi Tech Corp., a new, innovative computer software company. To induce Patty to join Hi Tech, the corporation offered her, in addition to her salary, the opportunity to purchase 1,000 shares of common stock at $5 a share, and an option to purchase an additional 1,000 shares each year for the next five years at $5 per share. Hi Tech stock is not publicly traded, but several investors recently paid $10 per share in private placements. The 1,000 shares Patty purchased when she joined Hi Tech must be resold to Hi Tech at $5 per share if Patty leaves the corporation any time within three years of the purchase. Thereafter, the shares need not be resold to Hi Tech unless Patty goes to work for a competitor within ten years of the date of purchase, in which case they must still be resold at $5 per share. Patty may transfer stock purchased pursuant to the options, but stock owned by a transferee is subject to the same restrictions to which it would be subject if owned by Patty. The options are not transferable and are exercisable only as long as Patty is an employee. Any stock purchased pursuant to the options will be subject to the same restrictions as the original stock. What are the income tax consequences of this arrangement for Patty and for Hi Tech?

(2)   What are the factors to be considered in advising Patty whether or not to make an election under IRC § 83(b) upon purchase of the stock?

(3)   What would be the amount and character of Patty's gain with respect to the original 1,000 shares if she made an IRC § 83(b) election and sold the stock eleven years later for $100 per share?

(b)   (1)   Eddie Exec is a vice-president of Gizmo Gadget Corp., a wholly owned subsidiary of Leviathan Corp. In August of last year, Eddie was granted, as a bonus, an option to purchase 3,000 shares of stock in Leviathan Corp. for $12 per share. At the time the option was granted, Leviathan Corp. was trading at $19 per share on the New York Stock Exchange. Identical options to buy Leviathan Corp. at $12 per share had recently sold privately for $8, but such options were not traded on an established market. Eddie's option was, by its express terms, nontransferable. This March, Eddie exercised his option when Leviathan was selling for $30 a share. One week later, he sold for $32 per share 1,000 shares of the Leviathan stock that he had just purchased. What are the tax consequences of these events for Eddie?

(2)   Would your answer to part (b)(1) be different if Eddie's option were actively traded on an established market?

(c)   (1)   How would your answer in part (b)(1) be different if Eddie's option were an incentive stock option under IRC § 422, and the Leviathan Corp. stock was trading at $10 per share on the day the option was granted?

(2)   What would be the amount and character of Eddie's gain if thirteen months after the date of the exercise of the option, he sold for $40 per share 1,000 of the Leviathan shares purchased pursuant to the incentive stock option?

(3)   What would be the amount and character of Eddie's gain if he sold 1,000 of the Leviathan shares for $40 per share twenty months after the date of exercise of the incentive stock option?

PROBLEM SET 40-3

¶ 40.05 INDIVIDUAL RETIREMENT ACCOUNTS

(a)   (1)   Ward and June have been married for several years. Both are under the age of 50. Ward manages a fast food restaurant, earning $35,000 per year. June makes $45,000 per year selling insurance. Neither of them participates in an employer-sponsored qualified pension or profit-sharing plan. If they each contribute $3,000 to a deductible individual retirement account (IRA) in 2002, how much will they be entitled to deduct on their joint return?

        (2)   Early the next year, they have a baby boy, Wally. Since June has the greater earning capacity, they decide she will continue to sell insurance, and Ward will stay home to take care of Wally. June's earned income is again $45,000; Ward earns nothing. What is the maximum IRA deduction for which they can qualify?

        (3)   In 2004, when Ward is still staying home taking care of Wally and their new son, Theodore, June's employer institutes a qualified pension plan, in which June became an "active participant." Her adjusted gross income (AGI) for the year is $80,000, and the total contributions to her qualified plan are $1,500. She also contributes $3,000 to her IRA and $3,000 to Ward's. May they deduct the IRA contributions?

        (4)   Many years later, when June is 60, she retires and begins receiving payments from her IRA, to which she had made a total of $16,000 deductible and $4,000 nondeductible contributions. She (or her estate) will receive a $2,000 distribution each year for twenty years, after which the IRA will be exhausted. How much of each distribution is taxable?

(b)   The year is 2004. Martha (an unmarried taxpayer) wants to make a contribution to an IRA, but she is uncertain whether she would be better off making a contribution to a regular IRA or to a Roth IRA. Which would be the better choice in each of the following situations?

        (1)   Martha has $3,000 she wants to devote to retirement savings this year. She meets the eligibility requirements for both IRA types. Her marginal tax rate this year is 30 percent, and her

best guess is that her marginal tax rate in her retirement years will be the same.

(2)   Martha has $3,000 she wants to devote to retirement savings this year. She meets the eligibility requirements for both IRA types. Her marginal tax rate this year is 30 percent, and her best guess is that her marginal tax rate in her retirement years will be lower (say, 20 percent).

(3)   Martha has $3,000 she wants to devote to retirement savings this year. She meets the eligibility requirements for both IRA types. Her marginal tax rate this year is 30 percent, and her best guess is that her marginal tax rate in her retirement years will be higher (say, 40 percent).

(4)   Martha wants to devote as much money to retirement savings this year as she possibly can. She meets the eligibility requirements for both IRA types. Her marginal tax rate this year is 30 percent, and her best guess is that her marginal tax rate in her retirement years will be the same.

(5)   Martha is an active participant in her employer's tax-favored pension plan. Her AGI is $90,000.

PROBLEM SET 40-4

¶ 40.06 COVERDELL EDUCATION SAVINGS ACCOUNTS; ¶ 40.07 QUALIFIED TUITION PROGRAMS

(a)   Grandpa (a widower) wants to save for his grandchildren's educations, but he is confused about the relative merits of qualified tuition programs (IRC § 529) and Coverdell education savings accounts (IRC § 530). Which tax-favored savings vehicle should he choose in each of the following situations?

(1)   His AGI is about $150,000.

(2)   He would like to make annual contributions of about $5,000 for each of his grandchildren.

(3)   His primary interest is financing the cost of sending his grandchildren to expensive private high schools.

(4)   His AGI is about $80,000, he wants to make an annual contribution of $2,000 for each grandchild, and he insists on being able to direct the investment of his contributions.

41

Installment Sales

¶¶ 41.01–41.05 (THE ENTIRE CHAPTER)

(a) (1) Landspec Co., a cash method taxpayer, sold a parcel of undeveloped land that it purchased as an investment five years ago for $60,000. The buyer paid Landspec $100,000 in cash and gave it a promissory note for $200,000, with 12 percent interest per annum (which you may assume is adequate), payable in four installments of $50,000 of principal plus accrued interest. Installments are payable every year for four years after the year of the sale. How should Landspec report its gain on the sale of the land, assuming that it does not make an IRC § 453(d) election?

   (2) Would your answer to part (a)(1) be different if Landspec were an accrual method taxpayer?

   (3) How would your answer to parts (a)(1) and (a)(2) be different if Landspec made an IRC § 453(d) election and the fair market value of the promissory note were $180,000?

   (4) How would your answer to part (a)(1) be different if the property sold were a commercial building (placed in service before 1987), and $60,000 of the gain on the sale was IRC § 1250 recapture income?

   (5) How would your answer to part (a)(1) be different if the property were an apartment building subject to a mortgage of $30,000, Landspec received $90,000 of cash in the year of sale, and the principal installments on the promissory note were $45,000 instead of $50,000 each?

   (6) How would your answer be different if the property were an apartment building subject to a mortgage of $120,000, Landspec received no cash at the closing, and the principal installments on the promissory note were $45,000 each?

   (7) How would your answer to part (a)(5) be different if the

purchaser were Larry Land, whose wife Louise owns 80 percent of the stock of Landspec, which is a corporation?

(b)   (1)   Ike Investor sold undeveloped land, which he had purchased several years ago for $5,000, to his daughter, Irene, for $15,000. His daughter paid for the land by giving Ike an unsecured promissory note for $15,000, with adequate interest, due four years from the date of sale. One year later, Irene sold the land for $20,000 cash. She eventually paid the note when due. What are the tax consequences to Ike and Irene?

    (2)   Would your answer to part (b)(1) be different if Irene sold the land for $12,000?

    (3)   Would your answer to part (b)(1) be different if Irene sold the land three years after she purchased it?

    (4)   Would your answer to part (b)(3) be different if the property involved were marketable securities, rather than land?

    (5)   Would your answer to part (b)(1) be different if the promissory note Irene gave to Ike required one principal payment of $7,500 after one year (i.e., in the same year that Irene sold the note), and a second principal payment of $7,500 at the end of four years, and the payments were made when due?

(c)   (1)   Last November, Violet Vendor sold a parcel of undeveloped land to Peter Purchaser for $100,000. Peter paid for the land by giving Violet a promissory note for $100,000, bearing adequate stated interest, due in five years. Violet purchased the land ten years ago for $10,000. In February, Violet sold the promissory note to the Last National Bank for $90,000. What are the tax consequences to Violet?

    (2)   Would your answer be different if instead of discounting the note, after ascertaining the value at which it could have been discounted, Violet gave the note to her daughter, Vera, who held the note to maturity? What will be the consequences to Vera when she collects the note?

    (3)   Would your answer be different if Violet died one year after the sale and bequeathed the promissory note to Vera?

    (4)   What would be your answer to parts (c)(2) and (c)(3) if Vera had been the purchaser and obligor on the note?

(5)   Would your answer to part (c)(1) be different if Violet sold the land to Leviathan Corp., which gave her a five-year bond of a class currently traded on the over-the-counter securities market, with a fair market value and redemption price of $100,000?

(d)   Georges Gizmo sold 100 percent of the outstanding stock of Gizmo Corp., in which he had a basis of $80,000, to Ernie Entrepreneur. (The Gizmo Corp. stock was not, of course, traded on any securities market.) The principal asset of Gizmo Corp. was a patent on the new improved gizmo, which was of speculative value; therefore, the purchase price was set equal to 2 percent of sales of gizmos for the remaining sixteen years of the life of the patent. Assume that payments worked out to be $40,000 for each of the first eight years and $20,000 for each of the last eight years. How should Georges report his gains, assuming he does not elect out of IRC § 453? How should he report his gains if he does elect out of IRC § 453?

(e)   (1)   To the extent that IRC § 453A imposes an interest charge on tax liability deferred under IRC § 453, is qualifying for deferral under IRC § 453 of any real advantage to a taxpayer?

        (2)   Should IRC § 453A be extended to cover all IRC § 453 installment obligations, regardless of amount?

42

Original Issue Discount and Other Unstated Interest Rules

¶¶ 42.01–42.04 (THE ENTIRE CHAPTER)

(a)　(1)　On December 31, 2002, Irene Investor paid $9,000 to purchase on the market a debenture bond issued in 1994 by Monolithic Industries, Inc. The bond had an issue price of $10,000, paid 8 percent interest per year and $10,000 upon maturity, and was due on December 31, 2004. What will be the character of Irene's gain upon redemption of the bond?

　　　(2)　What would be the character of Irene's gain if she sold the bond for $9,900 on September 30, 2004, three months before redemption?

(b)　Without doing any computations, how would your answers to part (a) differ if Irene had acquired the bond directly from Monolithic Industries, Inc., upon issue for $9,000?

(c)　Carl Condo sold his vacation condominium on Cherokee Island to Otto Ocean for $200,000. At the closing on July 1, Otto paid Carl $20,000 in cash and gave him a promissory note, secured by a mortgage, for $180,000. The note provided for no interest. The note was payable in installments of $20,000, due on July 1 of each of the next nine years. Carl's basis in his condominium was $40,000. May Carl report $160,000 of capital gain on the sale of his condominium? Why or why not?

(d)   Sarah Seller owned a large tract of undeveloped land with a basis of $2.5 million. She sold it to Barbara Buyer for no cash down and a note secured by the land. The note provided for no interest, and a single principal payment of $10 million in ten years. Using a discount rate equal to the applicable federal rate, compounded semiannually, the note had a present value of $4 million. Describe, in general terms, the tax consequences of this transaction to Sarah and Barbara.

44

Tax Returns, Rates, and Payments

PROBLEM SET 44-1

¶ 44.02 FILING STATUS—SEPARATE, JOINT, AND HEAD OF HOUSEHOLD RETURNS

(a)   Bill and Betty Bliss are a married couple, each of whom earns a salary of $50,000 a year. They have no children. They are very happily married, except for their concern over the income tax consequences of marriage. They decide to obtain a divorce, solely to save taxes. Accordingly, they are divorced on December 1 and thereafter continue to live together just as before. The divorce is valid under the laws of the state in which they live. Will they succeed in reducing their tax liability? If so, by how much?

(b)   Carl and Clara Couple are married. Each had a salary of $50,000 last year. They had no other income. Their only expense of relevance for tax purposes was $20,000 of uninsured medical expenses. All the medical expenses related to a serious injury incurred by Carl, and the expenses were paid solely by Carl. What advice would you give Carl and Clara concerning the filing of their income tax returns?

(c)   Should the marriage penalties and bonuses of current law be repealed? If so, how should the rate schedules in IRC § 1 be amended?

(d)   John and Jane Joint are a married couple. John is a bank vice-president, and Jane is a full-time homemaker. Over the last few months, John has been spending large amounts of money on luxury items, including a $60,000 Mercedes. Jane cannot understand where the money for these purchases has come from, and John refuses to explain. From a few comments John has made, Jane suspects John may be embezzling money from the bank. Should Jane agree to file a joint return with John?

(e)   (1)   In 2001, when Karen Kiddie was five years old, her grandmother gave her $100,000 worth of stock of Mega Corp. In 2002, Mega Corp. paid Karen $10,000 of dividends. Karen had no other income in 2002. Karen's parents filed a joint return for 2002, which reported $50,000 of taxable income. Karen has no brothers or sisters. Compute the tax on Karen's 2002 income.

        (2)   Karen's grandmother also gave her $10,000 worth of stock in Growth Corp., in which her grandmother had a $10,000 basis, at the same time as the gift of Mega Corp. stock. The policy of Growth Corp. has been to reinvest all of its earnings, rather than to pay any dividends. As a result of these reinvested earnings, Karen was able to sell her Growth Corp. stock for $30,000 when she was 14 years old. Will IRC § 1(g) apply in computing the tax on Karen's $20,000 gain?

45

Alternative Minimum Tax

PROBLEM SET 45-1

¶ 45.01 INTRODUCTION; ¶ 45.02 ALTERNATIVE MINIMUM TAXABLE INCOME; ¶ 45.03 COMPUTATION OF ALTERNATIVE MINIMUM TAX LIABILITY

(a)   Lisa Loophole, an unmarried taxpayer, received a $100,000 salary in 2002. She paid $5,000 of local real property tax on her home. She paid $4,000 interest on a $40,000 mortgage loan, which she incurred to purchase her home. She also paid $8,000 interest on $80,000 of home equity indebtedness. She gave undeveloped land, which she had held for investment for five years, to her church. The land was worth $30,000 at the time of the contribution, and her basis in the land was $5,000. Pursuant to an incentive stock option, she purchased stock in her employer's company with a fair market value of $20,000, at a price of $8,000 (except for IRC § 422, this would have resulted in $12,000 of income in the year she exercised the option, under IRC § 83). Assuming there is no other relevant information, calculate Lisa's federal income tax liability for 2002.

(b)   Fred and Marie, a married couple, had $90,000 of gross income last year. They have five children, ranging in age from two to ten. They claimed the following itemized deductions:

Interest on home equity debt	$3,000
State income tax	$5,000
Local real property tax	$4,000

Assuming there is no other relevant information, calculate their federal income tax liability for last year. Do they have any AMT liability?

(c)   The official policy explanation for the alternative minimum tax (AMT) is as follows:

Although [tax preferences] may provide incentives for worthy goals, they become counterproductive when taxpayers are allowed to use them to avoid virtually all tax liability. The ability of high-income individuals . . . to pay little or no tax undermines respect for the entire tax system and, thus, for the incentive provisions themselves. In addition, even aside from public perceptions, the committee believes that it is inherently unfair for high income individuals . . . to pay little or no tax due to their ability to utilize various tax preferences.

S. Rep. No. 313, 99th Cong., 2d Sess. 518–519 (1986). Do you find this explanation persuasive, or does the AMT demonstrate that the attitude of Congress towards tax preferences is hopelessly confused?